Research on Legumes - Updates and Prospects

Edited by Naser A. Anjum, Asim Masood, Shahid Umar and Nafees A. Khan

Published in London, United Kingdom

Research on Legumes - Updates and Prospects
http://dx.doi.org/10.5772/intechopen.1011202
Edited by Naser A. Anjum, Asim Masood, Shahid Umar and Nafees A. Khan

Contributors
Abdul Enam, Aggrey Keya Osogo, Alexander S. Lukatkin, Ali Hassan Anany, Asim Masood, Asmaa H. Zaki, Bahaa Abugammie, Beatrice Victor Mwaipopo, Consuelo Penella, Deusdedith R. Mbanzibwa, Elisa Gorbe, Iqra Khan, Irene Moreno-Valle, Luseko Amos Chilagane, Michael Lucas Daud, Mohamed A. S. Khalifa, Nafees A. Khan, Naser A. Anjum, Palaniswamy Thangavel, Papias H. Binagwa, Rizah Akbar, Salma O. Mohhamed, Sate Sahle, Shahid Umar, Susan Nchimbi-Msolla, Tehreem Fatima

First published in London, United Kingdom, 2026 by IntechOpen
IntechOpen is the global imprint of INTECHOPEN LIMITED, registered in England and Wales, registration number: 11086078, 167-169 Great Portland Street, London, W1W 5PF, United Kingdom

For EU product safety concerns: IN TECH d.o.o., Prolaz Marije Krucifikse Kozulić 3, 51000 Rijeka, Croatia, info@intechopen.com or visit our website at intechopen.com.

British Library Cataloguing-in-Publication Data
A catalogue record for this book is available from the British Library

Research on Legumes - Updates and Prospects
Edited by Naser A. Anjum, Asim Masood, Shahid Umar and Nafees A. Khan
p. cm.

This title is part of the Agricultural Sciences Book Series, Volume 44
Topic: Agronomy and Horticulture
Series Editor: W. James Grichar
Topic Editors: Murat Helvaci and Olga Panfilova

Print ISBN 978-1-80631-598-7
Online ISBN 978-1-80631-597-0
eBook (PDF) ISBN 978-1-80631-599-4
ISSN 3029-052X

If disposing of this product, please recycle the paper responsibly.

IntechOpen Book Series

Agricultural Sciences

Volume 44

Aims and Scope of the Series

The importance of agriculture cannot be overstated. It helps sustain life, as it gives us the food we need to survive and provides opportunities for economic well-being. Agriculture helps people prosper around the world and combines the creativity, imagination, and skill involved in planting crops and raising animals with modern production methods and new technologies. This series includes two main topics: Agronomy and Horticulture, and Animal Farming. This series will help readers better understand the intricacies of production agriculture and provide the new knowledge that is required to be successful. The success of a farmer in modern agriculture requires knowledge of events happening locally as well as globally that impact input decisions and ultimately determine net profit.

Meet the Series Editor

W. James Grichar has been employed with Texas A&M AgriLife Research for over 45 years with an emphasis on research in agronomy, plant pathology, and weed science. He obtained his BS from Texas A&M in 1972 and his Masters of Plant Protection in 1975. He has published 195 journal articles, over 330 research reports and briefs, 11 book chapters, and over 300 abstracts of profession meetings. He also directs research in many crops including corn, grain sorghum, peanuts, and sesame. He has held various positions in different professional societies including the American Peanut Research and Education Society, Southern Weed Science Society, and Texas Plant Protection Conference in addition to being Associate Editor for Peanut Science and Weed Technology. Significant accomplishments have included spearheading efforts to determine the optimum planting time for soybean production along the upper Texas Gulf Coast. These efforts have shown growers that soybean yields can be improved by 10 to 20% by following a late March to early April plant date. He also has been instrumental in developing a herbicide program for peanut production in the south Texas growing region. Through the development and use of herbicides that are effective against major weed problems in the south Texas region, peanut yields have increased by 25 to 30%.

Meet the Volume Editors

Dr. Naser A. Anjum obtained a Ph.D. in Botany from Jamia Hamdard, New Delhi, India, and received postdoctoral research training at the University of Aveiro, Portugal; the Agricultural Biotechnology Research Center, Academia Sinica, Taiwan; and Aligarh Muslim University, Aligarh, India. Dr. Anjum has made significant contributions to the biology of plant/crop-environment adaptation. He has received prestigious research awards from reputable funding agencies, including the Portuguese Foundation for Science and Technology, the Council of Scientific and Industrial Research (New Delhi, India), and the Department of Biotechnology (New Delhi, India). Dr. Anjum has published more than 125 peer-reviewed papers, edited over 20 books and journal special issues, and also authored 2 books. He is an elected fellow of the Linnean Society of London, the Indian Botanical Society, the International Society of Environmental Botanists (India), and the National Academy of Biological Sciences (India).

Dr. Asim Masood has unveiled major insights into the impacts of abiotic stresses (metals, salt, and temperature) and the underlying physiological/ biochemical mechanisms in crop plants. He received a Start-Up Career Grant from the University Grants Commission, New Delhi (India), and a DST-SERB Young Scientist Project from the Department of Science and Technology, New Delhi (India). His research interests include the involvement of ethylene in S-mediated alleviation of Cd, ethylene-mediated regulation of photosynthesis as a result of reduced glucose sensitivity, ethylene-mediated modulation of gibberellic acid-induced S-assimilation under Cd-stress, and ethylene-mediated reversal of salinity impacts involving ethylene-abscisic acid coordination. Dr. Masood has authored over 70 research articles in esteemed national and international journals, contributed 14 book chapters, edited 4 books, and authored 1 book.

Prof. Shahid Umar has identified the major strategies for developing abiotic stress-tolerant crops by modulating tolerance mechanisms at both physiological and molecular levels, deciphered the importance of N-metabolism in cereals and leafy vegetables, enhanced N-use efficiency, and developed synergism between primary nutrients and growth under varied environmental conditions. Prof. Umar has 10 volumes (including 1 authored book) to his credit and has participated in research projects funded by agencies, including the International Potash Research Institute in Switzerland. For his significant contributions to potassium nutrition management to improve crop yield and quality, Prof. Umar has received several awards, including the 2003 IPI-FAI International Award from the International Potash Institute, Basel, Switzerland, and the Fertilizer Association of India.

Prof. Nafees A. Khan has contributed to abiotic tolerance mechanisms in relation to a positive shift in the source-sink relationship. This mechanism mainly involves ethylene and its coordination with other major phytohormones, which mediate signal transduction and modulate the ascorbate-glutathione system. His path-breaking R&D contributions in physio-biochemistry of abiotic stress tolerance strategies led to the publication of several journal articles. Prof. Khan was deemed a Highly Cited Researcher for five consecutive years (2019-2023) and also received the Clarivate India Research Excellence Citation Award in 2023. He has published over 200 research articles, boasts an H-index of 85, and edited 27 books (including 3 authored volumes). Prof. Khan serves on the editorial boards of reputable journals and has guest-edited several special issues in specialized and multidisciplinary journals. Prof. Khan is an elected fellow of important learned societies of international (Linnean Society, London, United Kingdom) and national (National Academy of Sciences, National Academy of Agricultural Sciences, Indian Society for Plant Physiology, and Indian Botanical Society) repute.

Contents

Preface **XIII**

Chapter 1 **1**
Introductory Chapter: Research on Legumes – Updates and Prospects
by Naser A. Anjum, Asim Masood, Shahid Umar and Nafees A. Khan

Chapter 2 **13**
Legumes: Nutritional, Health, Agricultural and Environmental Benefits and Cultivation Practices
by Sate Sahle

Chapter 3 **23**
Potential of Legume Landraces to Combat Hidden Hunger
by Elisa Gorbe, Irene Moreno-Valle and Consuelo Penella

Chapter 4 **47**
Global Legume Production, Constraints and Future Prospects
by Aggrey Keya Osogo

Chapter 5 **71**
Neglected and Underutilized Legume Crops: Key Insights into Origin, Botany, Benefits, Constraints and Recent Research Focus
by Naser A. Anjum, Asim Masood, Iqra Khan, Abdul Enam, Tehreem Fatima, Rizah Akbar, Palaniswamy Thangavel, Alexander S. Lukatkin, Shahid Umar and Nafees A. Khan

Chapter 6 **91**
Underutilized and Wild Legumes: New Frontiers
by Mohamed A. S. Khalifa, Asmaa H. Zaki, Ali Hassan Anany and Bahaa Abugammie

Chapter 7 **125**
Bean Rust Disease in the Genomics Era: Pathogen Diversity, Resistance Breeding and Field Impact
by Michael Lucas Daud, Papias H. Binagwa, Susan Nchimbi-Msolla, Deusdedith R. Mbanzibwa, Beatrice Victor Mwaipopo, Salma O. Mohhamed and Luseko Amos Chilagane

Preface

Proteins are among six key nutrient categories found in human foods, which are essential for good human health, reproduction, and growth. The other five key nutrient categories include carbohydrates, lipids (primarily fats and oils), vitamins, minerals, and water. Composed of amino acids, proteins are among the major constituents of a healthy and balanced human diet. Proteins are essential for building and repairing tissues, producing hormones and enzymes, and supporting various bodily functions. The requirement for proteins in the human diet can be met by both animal- and plant-based proteins. However, the best protein sources in the human diet depend on consumers' needs and dietary preferences. Interestingly, the human body cannot produce all nine essential amino acids (like histidine, isoleucine, leucine, lysine, methionine, phenylalanine, threonine, tryptophan, and valine). Hence, these nine essential amino acids must be obtained from animal-based foods such as meat, poultry, fish, eggs, and dairy products. Unfortunately, animal-based diets are considered unsustainable, inefficient, environmentally unfriendly, and unhealthy. In particular, the average animal-based proteins produced require 11 times more fossil energy, 4-26 times more water, and 6-17 times more land than plant-based proteins.

Legumes (a group of plants in the family Fabaceae or Leguminosae with a rough number of taxa between 670-750, and species between 18,000-19,000) comprise both grain legumes (whose dry seeds are consumed by humans for food) and pasture (or forage) legumes (which are cultivated to feed domestic animals, and/or used as a green manure for improving soil fertility and structure; e.g., *Medicago sativa; Trifolium pratense; T. repens; T. hybridum; T. incarnatum; Vicia sativa; V. benghalensis; V. villosa; V. narbonensis; Lotus corniculatus; Onobrychis viciifolia; Sericea lespedeza,* and *Lespedeza cuneata*).

Mainly grown as pulses, grain legumes provide food for humans and stand second to none in terms of their significance as excellent sources of dietary protein, high protein content (16-50%), balanced amino acid profiles, and affordability. Based on plant utility and economy, legumes can be categorized into: (i) **major legumes** (popular and common with well-established domestication and cultivation; e.g., *Glycine max; Vigna unguiculata; Arachis hypogaea; Phaseolus vulgaris; Pisum sativum;* and *Cicer arietinum*), (ii) **minor legumes** (less known, less exploited, neglected, and considered underutilized; e.g., *Psophocarpus tetragonolobus; Cajanus cajan; Lablab purpureus; Phaseolus lunatus; Canavalia sp.; Vigna mungo; V. subterranea; V. angularies;* and *Sphenostylis stenocarpa*), and (iii) **minor wild legumes** (having potential for exploitation for food, medicine, agriculture; e.g., *Kerstingiella geocarpa; Tylosema esculentum; Vigna ambacensis; V. vexillata, V. luteola, V. oblongifolia,* and *V. racemosa*).

Though typically low in some amino acids (like methionine and cysteine), most legumes possess appreciable amounts of lysine, leucine, isoleucine, phenylalanine, threonine, valine, and tryptophan. Regarded as a precious gift of nature to mankind and also often nicknamed as "poor man's meat", legumes are also loaded with dietary fibre (10-23%), minerals (like folate, Fe, Mg and K), carbohydrates, sugars, vitamins, mono- and poly-unsaturated fatty acids, and important non-nutritional bioactive components (like polyphenolics, lectins, phytate and trypsin inhibitors). Several human health benefits linked to the consumption of grain legumes include a lower risk of cardiovascular disease, type 2 diabetes mellitus, certain cancers, reduced obesity risk, and improved digestive health.

Legumes also significantly contribute to the improvement of soil and environmental health. To this end, legumes perform atmospheric N2 Fixation (by maintaining a unique symbiotic relationship with N2-fixing bacteria/Rhizobium in their root nodules) that frees legumes from the need to access soil sources of fixed N, reduces the need for synthetic fertilizers, and contributes to soil health. Legumes contribute to reducing the emission of greenhouse gases (GHG), as they release 5-7 times less GHG per unit area (versus other crops). Additionally, legumes help mitigate climate change (via carbon sequestration) by employing their deep root systems. Legumes are an important sustainable option for farmers, owing to their ability to be cultivated across different soil types and their need for less water and fertilizer under a variety of climates.

Despite the widely recognized roles of legumes in (agricultural and environmental) sustainability and human food and nutritional security, several constraints on legumes are significantly hampering their growth, development, productivity, and utilization. The list of important constraints requiring immediate global attention includes: agronomic challenges (like low soil fertility, weed competition, and pests and diseases); environmental challenges (like abiotic stresses/ adverse environmental conditions like drought, heat, and salinity, particularly in semi-arid and arid tropics); genetic challenges (like narrow genetic base, low resistance levels for pests, diseases, and abiotic stresses); consumption challenges (like low digestibility, antinutritional factors, and stigmatization as the food of the poor); and socioeconomic challenges (like limited market access, low yield and lack of government support).

Notably, the rapidly increasing human population and severe environmental degradation are two interconnected challenges that significantly impact global food and nutritional security. The estimated current global population (about 9.0 billion people) is projected to reach 8.5 billion by 2030, potentially reaching up to 9.8 billion by 2050. This projected global population growth would increase, putting immense pressure on food production systems. The unsustainable food production systems adopted to fulfill the continuously growing global food demand are leading to significant soil degradation, water scarcity, and biodiversity loss, all of which threaten long-term food security (the access of every individual to sufficient, safe, and nutritious food). Climate change is further exacerbating these constraints by impacting legume health, yield, and availability.

Given above, this book aims to: introduce the theme of the book and enlighten the significance of legumes in sustainably securing food, nutrition, and the good health of humans and the environment for the rising global population; overview the global legume production, constraints and prospects; highlight the nutritional, health, agricultural, and environmental benefits of legumes and the key practices involved in their cultivation; discuss the potential of legume landraces in combating global hidden hunger; briefly enlightens key insights into origin, botany, benefits, constraints, and recent focus of research on neglected and underutilized legume crops; appraise literature on new frontiers related to underutilized and wild legumes; and present important aspects on bean rust in the genomics era.

This book would serve as an excellent resource for students, researchers, scientists, plant biologists, and agronomists engaged in teaching and research, offering significant insights into various aspects of legumes in the context of (agricultural and environmental) sustainability, (animal) human food and nutritional security, and sustainable crop production.

We take this opportunity to express our thanks to IntechOpen for providing a platform and showcasing our work. We are also thankful to Publishing Process Manager, Mrs. Laura Divic, for her efficiency and guidance, which helped us to accomplish this book project. Our sincere gratitude also goes to the chapter authors who contributed their time and expertise to this book. Without their support, this book would not have become a reality.

Naser A. Anjum, Asim Masood and Nafees A. Khan
Department of Botany,
Aligarh Muslim University,
Aligarh, Uttar Pradesh, India

Shahid Umar
Department of Botany,
School of Chemical & Life Sciences,
Jamia Hamdard,
New Delhi, India

Chapter 1

Introductory Chapter: Research on Legumes – Updates and Prospects

Naser A. Anjum, Asim Masood, Shahid Umar and Nafees A. Khan

1. Introduction

1.1 Background

Securing food, nutrition, and the good health of humans and the environment for the rising global population (which is projected to reach 9.7 billion by 2050) is the defining interdisciplinary research focus of the current decade. In order to fulfill these goals, there is a pressing need to transform current food systems into ones that are sustainable, equitable, and resilient. Current food production needs to be increased by 60–70% while simultaneously reducing the environmental footprint of the agriculture sector globally. Securing food and nutrition requires consistent access to a diverse, nutrient-dense diet comprising whole grains, lean proteins, fruits, vegetables, and healthy fats to meet essential nutrient needs. To this end, legumes (members of the Leguminosae/Fabaceae family/pea family), often referred to as the "poor man's meat," are foundational to a balanced, sustainable diet. They offer high-quality plant protein, complex carbohydrates, and fiber. Moreover, being low in fat and rich in complex carbohydrates, most essential amino acids, iron, and folate, legumes help reduce the risk of potential chronic diseases [1–4].

1.2 Fabaceae (Leguminosae) family and its members

Commonly known as the legume, pea, or bean family, the Fabaceae (or Leguminosae) family is the third-largest family of flowering plants and comprises roughly 750 genera/taxa and over 19,000–20,000 species of trees, shrubs, herbs, and climbers (see **Figure 1**). Owing to the availability of nitrogen-fixing nodules in their roots, legumes are critical for soil fertility and sustainable agriculture. Pod-like fruits (legumes; dry, dehiscent, or indehiscent), pinnately compound or trifoliate leaves (with a pulvinus/swollen leaf base), and zygomorphic flowers (often papilionaceous) are other key features of the Fabaceae (Leguminosae) family (see **Figure 2**). Based mainly on flower structure (flower symmetry and petal arrangement), the Fabaceae (Leguminosae) family is traditionally divided into three distinct sub-families: Faboideae (or Papilionoideae), Caesalpinioideae, and Mimosoideae (see **Figure 3**). Due to their high nutritional value, low cost, and long storage life, edible seeds of leguminous crop plants (food legumes: pulses and oilseeds) are considered staple foods worldwide. On one hand, pulses are dry seeds, possess low fat and high protein/fiber, and are consumed in dried, sprouted, or fresh forms, serving as crucial,

 IntechOpen

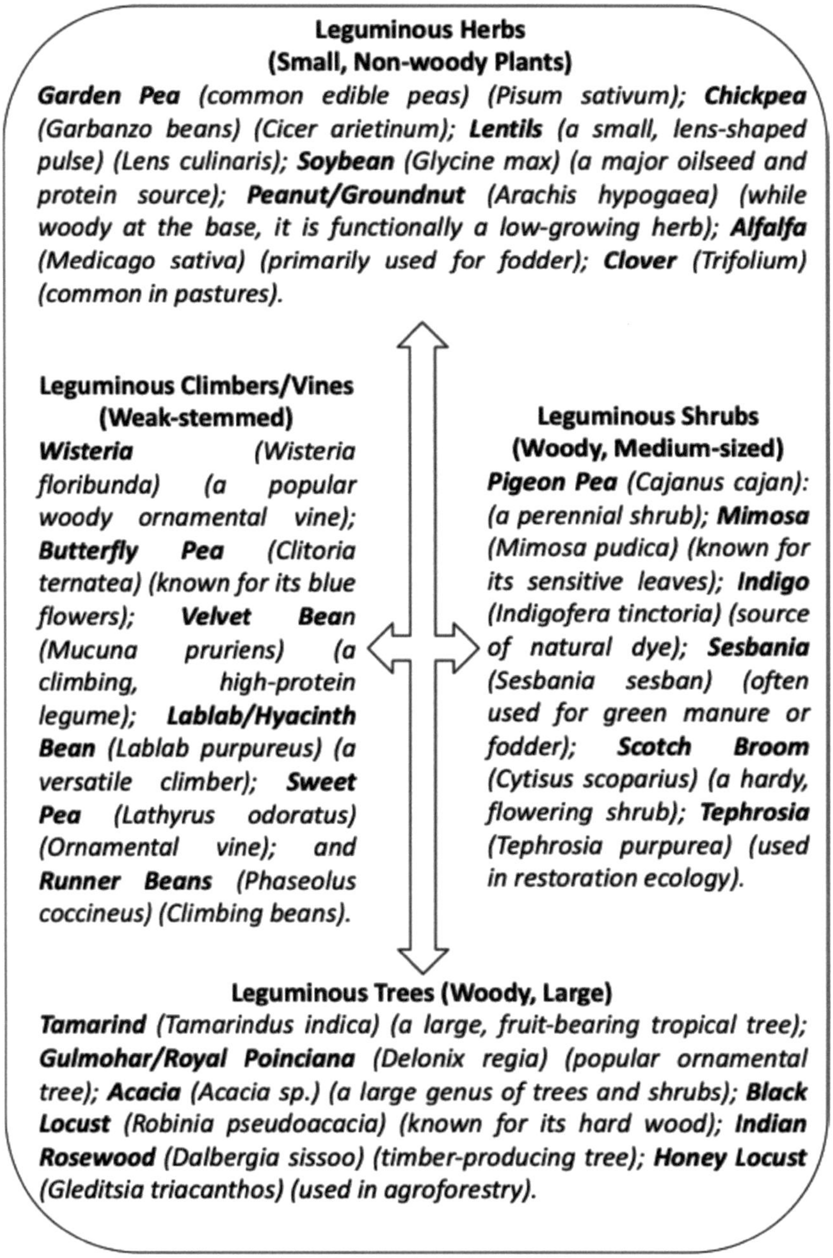

Figure 1.
Representative examples of legumes classified by their growth habits.

cost-effective, and sustainable protein sources worldwide. On the other hand, oilseed legumes are legumes with significantly high oil content and are mainly used for oils and/or as food [5, 6] (see **Figure 4**).

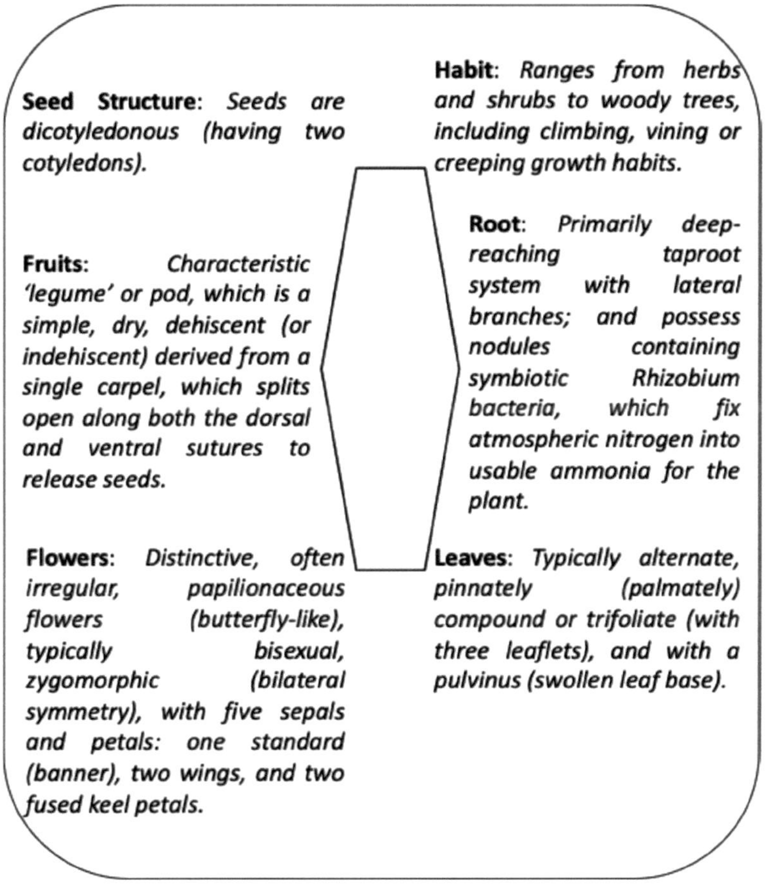

Figure 2.
Representation of key botanical characteristics of legumes.

2. Legumes in regions exhibiting half of the projected population growth

Interestingly, over half of the projected increase in global population growth (which is projected to reach 9.7 billion by 2050) is concentrated in nine countries: India, Nigeria, Pakistan, the Democratic Republic of the Congo, Ethiopia, Tanzania, Indonesia, Egypt, and the United States of America (see **Figures 5** and **6**). India is expected to surpass China as the world's most populous country around 2027, whereas the population in sub-Saharan Africa is expected to double by 2050 [7]. Notably, legume crops (pulses and oilseed legumes) are vital for food security, soil health, and nutrition across the aforementioned nine countries, where legume crop cultivation practices range from smallholder subsistence farming to large-scale mechanized agriculture [8].

3. Legumes and global food security

Vital to global food security, legumes significantly offer a sustainable, protein-rich, and affordable food source. By strengthening agriculture through nitrogen

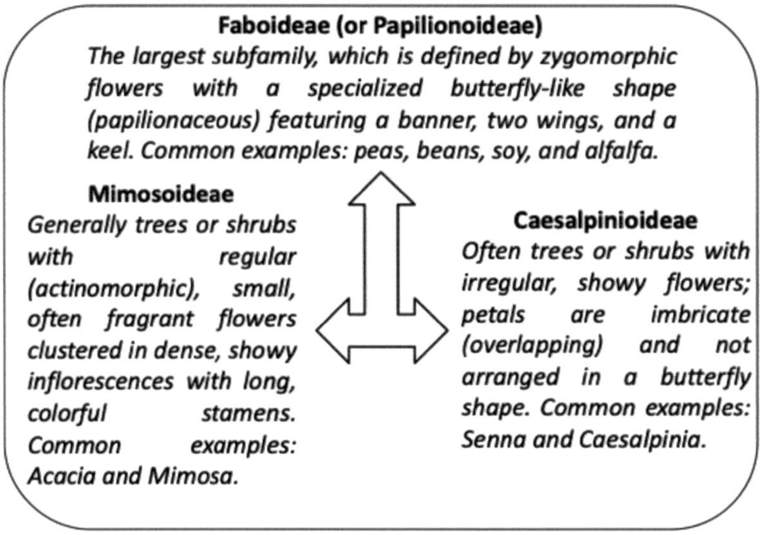

Figure 3.
Representation of key sub-families of Fabaceae (or Leguminosae) and their important characteristics.

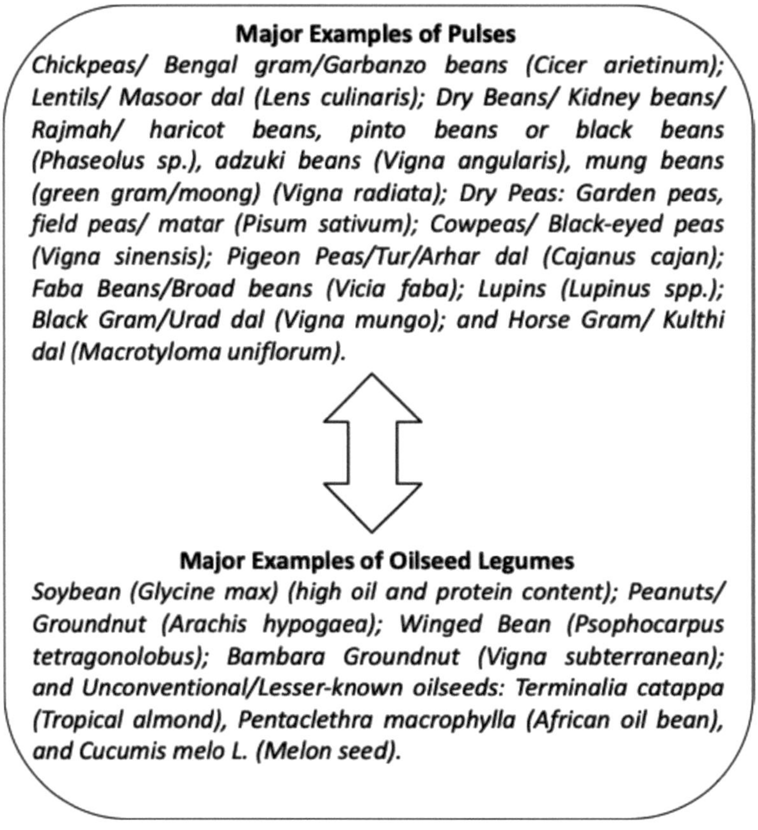

Figure 4.
Representative examples of pulses and oilseed legumes.

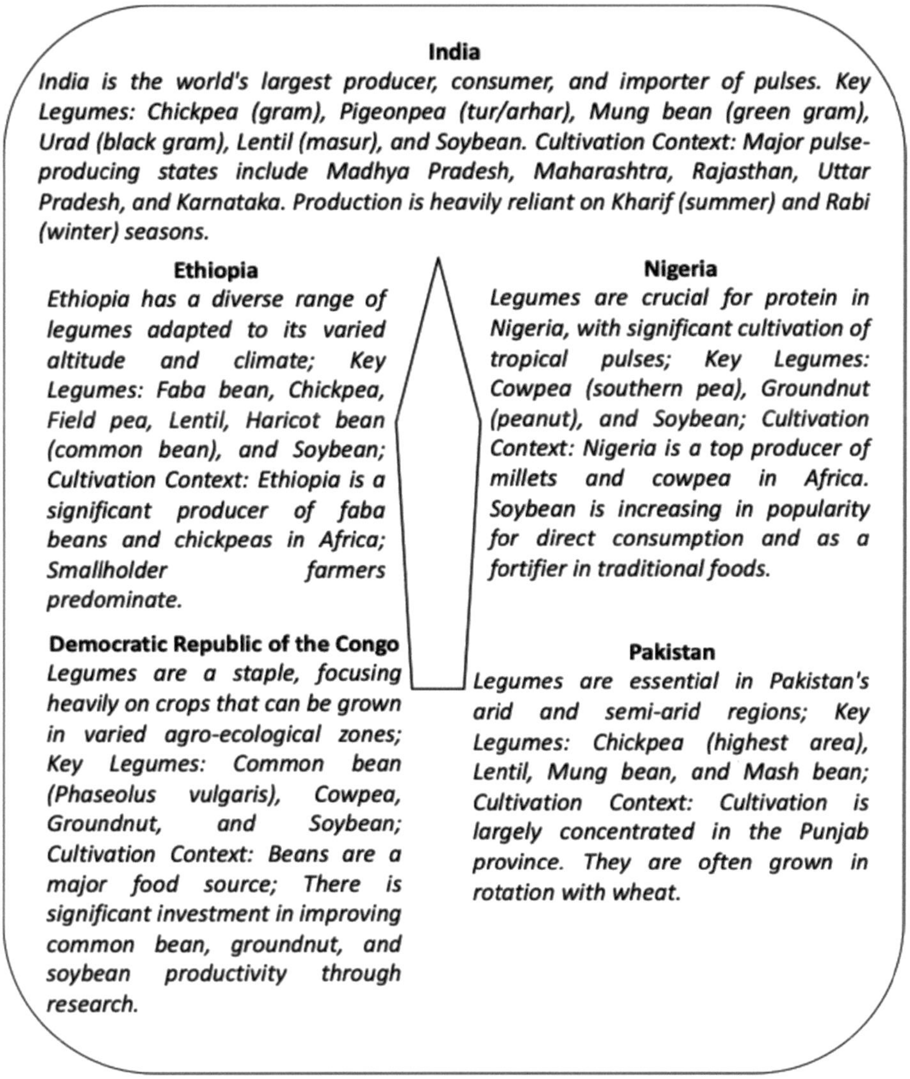

Figure 5.
Representation of the status of legumes in regions exhibiting half of the projected population growth (India, Nigeria, Pakistan, Democratic Republic of the Congo, and Ethiopia).

fixation, enhancing soil fertility, improving water management, and adapting to climate change, legume crops provide crucial nourishment for a growing population while supporting sustainable farming practices. Legume crops help secure food through: (i) acting as nutritional powerhouses (because legumes are high in plant-based proteins, dietary fiber, iron, folate, and zinc, thereby helping combat malnutrition and prevent chronic diseases such as diabetes and cardiovascular conditions); (ii) supporting sustainable agriculture (involving rhizobial symbiosis, legumes are able to fix atmospheric nitrogen into the soil, thereby reducing the need for chemical fertilizers and increasing the productivity of subsequent crops); (iii) exhibiting climate resilience (since legumes are often hardy, they provide

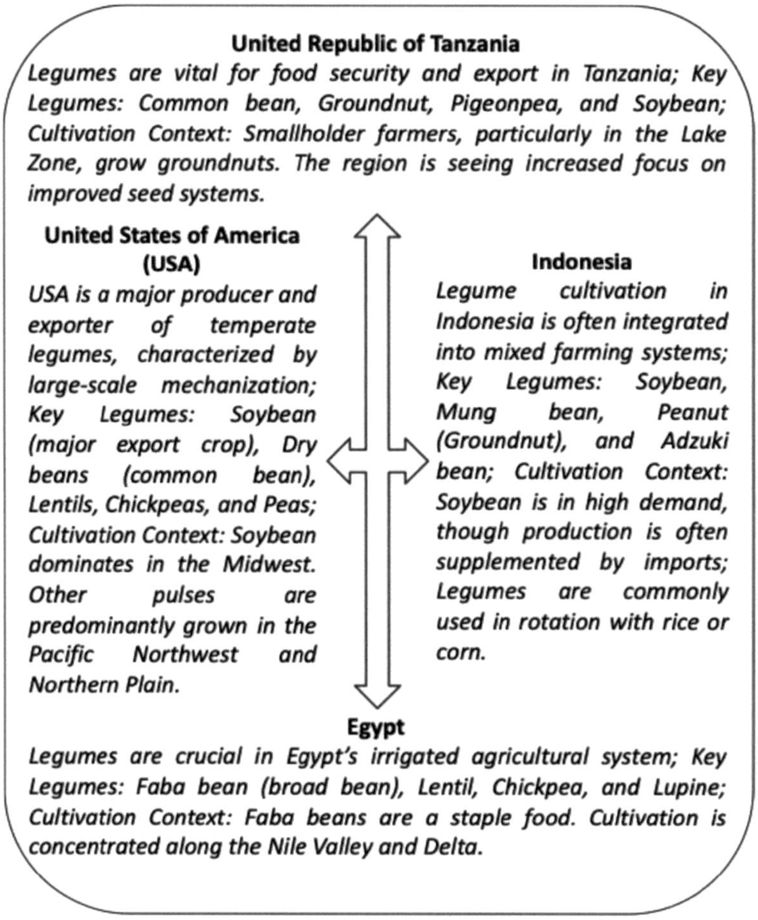

Figure 6.
Representation of the status of legumes in regions exhibiting half of the projected population growth (United Republic of Tanzania, Indonesia, Egypt, and United States of America).

a reliable food source even in adverse conditions caused by climate change, such as drought or poor soil quality); and (iv) promoting cost-effectiveness (as cost-effective staples, legumes enhance household food security, particularly in developing countries, and offer opportunities for farmers to increase income through improved crop varieties) [9–12].

4. Legumes and global nutritional security

Legumes are excellent sources of plant-based proteins, dietary fiber, and essential minerals (iron, zinc, and magnesium). Moreover, legumes offer a significant, sustainable, and affordable alternative to meat and provide essential amino acids crucial for muscle growth and repair. Legumes are rich in essential minerals (like iron, potassium, and phosphorus) and vitamins (like B-vitamins, including folate). Given these, legumes-based foods perform various physiological functions in the human body. Additionally, legumes also contain bioactive compounds (e.g., phenolic acids, flavonoids, carotenoids, and saponins), which significantly offer antioxidant properties and provide anti-inflammatory and antioxidant benefits. Interestingly, due to their high fiber content and low glycemic index, legumes help maintain steady blood sugar levels, promote satiety, and improve digestive health. Regular and optimal consumption of legumes has been widely linked to lower risks of cardiovascular disease, high blood pressure, and certain cancers [13–15].

5. Legumes and soil health security

Legume crops significantly improve soil health by fixing atmospheric nitrogen through symbiotic bacteria, increasing soil organic matter, and improving soil structure. In addition, legume crops are involved in promoting a diverse, active microbiome, enhancing phosphorus availability, boosting water-holding capacity, and reducing erosion. Acting as "nature's nitrogen fertilizer factory" (through their ability to fix atmospheric nitrogen in symbiosis with rhizobia bacteria), legume crops often supply about 50–90% of their own nitrogen needs and also leave behind residual nitrogen for subsequent crops. Moreover, legumes are indispensable for restoring soil fertility and supporting sustainable land development. In summary, legumes secure soil health through (i) enhancing soil physical properties (which involves improved soil structure, increased porosity, and reduced erosion); (ii) improving soil chemical properties (which involves biological nitrogen fixation, increased C-sequestration, nutrient cycling and P-availability, and soil amendment); and (iii) enhancing soil biological properties (which involves stimulated microbial diversity, improved tripartite symbiosis, and weed and pathogen suppression) [16, 17].

6. Legumes and environmental sustainability

Legumes offer a "win-win" scenario for both environmental protection and agricultural productivity through their unique biological abilities to reduce the need for synthetic inputs, restore soil health, and eventually transform food systems to be more sustainable. Contributions of legumes to environmental sustainability involve the following: (i) Natural fixation of atmospheric nitrogen-mediated pollution reduction – This involves a unique symbiotic relationship between legumes and Rhizobia bacteria in their root nodules, allowing them to fix atmospheric nitrogen directly into the soil. This, in turn, significantly decreases or eliminates the need for chemical nitrogen fertilizers. Additionally, legumes contribute to greenhouse gas-emission mitigation, as they emit five to seven times less greenhouse gas per unit area than other crops. (ii) Soil health improvement – Legumes enhance soil structure, increase fertility, promote carbon sequestration, and aid in salinity management. (iii) Climate change resilience and resource efficiency – Legumes contribute to water savings, abiotic stress tolerance, and energy efficiency. (iv) Biodiversity and cropping systems – Legumes play a vital role in crop rotation and intercropping, which are essential for breaking disease and pest cycles, thereby reducing the need for pesticides. Additionally, underutilized legumes, often referred to as "forgotten gems," are rediscovered for their ability to thrive in poor soils, helping conserve agricultural biodiversity. (v) Transition to sustainable diets – Legumes can replace animal protein due to their availability as a high-quality, plant-based protein source, comprising 17–30% of dry weight. They also have a lower ecological "hoofprint," as replacing imported legume-based feed with locally grown legumes often reduces greenhouse gas emissions significantly per unit of milk produced [12, 18–20].

7. Current research trends in legumes

Enhancing climate resilience, improving nutritional value, and optimizing the role of legumes in sustainable agriculture are among the major focuses of current research on legumes. Key trends in research on legumes include the following: (i) climate-resilient breeding (which involves research on developing legume varieties that withstand climate change, water scarcity, and drought stress to ensure food security); (ii) sustainable agriculture and soil health (which emphasizes research on the role of legumes in enhancing soil nitrogen, improving soil ecology, and reducing the need for chemical fertilizers); (iii) single-cell omics and molecular biology (which involves advanced research techniques, such as spatial transcriptomics, being used to study root nodule symbiosis and plant-microbe signaling at high resolution); (iv) nutritional and food technology (which involves the expansion of investigations into using legume proteins as high-value, sustainable, and hypoallergenic alternatives in food formulations, such as egg substitutes); (v) bioactive compounds and biopesticides (which involves the identification of bioactive compounds like lectins and proteinase inhibitors in legumes to serve as natural, sustainable pesticides against insect herbivores); and (vi) digital agriculture and post-harvesting (which involves the application of machine learning and intelligent sensors for improving the quality, sorting, and processing of legume products) [21–24].

8. Conclusions and future prospects

This chapter introduced the importance of transforming current food systems to be sustainable, equitable, and resilient in order to secure food, nutrition, and the good health of both humans and the environment for the rising global population, which is the defining interdisciplinary research focus of the current decade; briefly overviewed key aspects of the Fabaceae (Leguminosae) family and important characteristics of its members; highlighted the status of legumes in regions exhibiting half of the projected population growth; illuminated the major contributions of legumes to global food security, nutritional security, soil health security, and environmental sustainability; and also overviewed the current trends in research on legumes. Despite the numerous benefits mentioned above, most legumes are currently underutilized in many diets across the globe.

Given above, considering the briefly explained below categorized key future research themes for legumes may act as feasible and strong strategies for maximizing the role of legumes in achieving "Zero Hunger" (UN Sustainable Development Goal 2). First, the legume breeding and genetics theme (aimed at climate resilience and yield) may focus on investigations into climate-smart varieties (which may involve the development of legumes resistant to abiotic stresses such as heat, drought, salinity, and waterlogging); "omics" technologies (which may focus on the utilization of genomics, transcriptomics, and proteomics in speeding up genetic gains, and high-throughput sequencing for identifying traits for drought tolerance and yield stability); genome editing (where CRISPR and other gene-editing tools may be applied for improving specific traits, such as pod borer resistance, Fusarium wilt resistance, and reduced allergenicity); and underutilized/orphan legumes (which may involve the genetic improvement of neglected species for enhancing food security in marginal environments). Second, legume research connected with sustainable agriculture and soil health may focus on nitrogen fixation optimization (where researching the microbiome of the legume–rhizobia symbiosis may be done to maximize nitrogen input into the soil, reducing reliance on synthetic fertilizers); regenerative agriculture (where legumes may be integrated into cropping systems (intercropping, cover crops), which, in turn, would improve soil health, organic matter, and biodiversity); and biocontrol agents (which may involve the utilization of legume crops in rotations for reducing soilborne pathogens and pests, and eventually supporting low-intensity farming). Third, research on legumes in the context of nutrition, health, and processing biofortification may focus on increasing the iron and zinc content in seeds (to address global nutritional deficiencies), protein functionality (aimed at enhancing the functional properties (emulsification, gelation, foaming) of legume proteins for use in meat and dairy alternatives), addressing anti-nutritional factors (which may focus on improving digestibility and flavor by using breeding and processing techniques for removing "beany" flavors and selected anti-nutritional factors, e.g., phytic acid), and nutraceutical value (which may involve investigations into the role of legumes in preventing chronic diseases, e.g., cardiovascular diseases, diabetes, and cancer, through their high-quality protein and bioactive compounds).

Author details

Naser A. Anjum[1*], Asim Masood[1], Shahid Umar[2] and Nafees A. Khan[1]

1 Department of Botany, Aligarh Muslim University, Aligarh, India

2 Department of Botany, School of Chemical and Life Sciences, Jamia Hamdard, New Delhi, India

*Address all correspondence to: naanjum1@myamu.ac.in

References

[1] Hamad A, Tayel A. Food 2050 concept: Trends that shape the future of food. Journal of Future Foods. 2025;**6** (6):1053–1066

[2] Raposo A, Saraiva A. Nutrition and food security for all: A step towards the future. Nutrients. 2025;**17**(7):1241

[3] Roy A, Moradkhani H, Mekonnen M, Moftakhari H, Magliocca N. Towards strategic interventions for global food security in 2050. Science of the Total Environment. 2024;**954**:176811

[4] Suleiman MK. Global distribution of arid lands: Opportunities and constraints for agriculture and food security. In: Suleiman MK, Shahid SA, editors. Fostering Arid Lands Agriculture in the Face of Climate Change: Mitigation and Adaptation Synergy. Cham, Switzerland: Springer Nature; 2026. p. 3–24

[5] Anwar R, Borbi M, Rakha A. Significance and the use of legumes in developing weaning foods with a balanced nutrition-a review. Legume Science. 2024;**6**(3):e249

[6] Schmidt HDO, Oliveira VRD. Overview of the incorporation of legumes into new food options: An approach on versatility, nutritional, technological, and sensory quality. Foods. 2023;**12**(13):2586

[7] United Nations. 9.7 billion on Earth by 2050, but growth rate slowing, says new UN population report. United Nations. 2019; www.un.org/en/academic-impact/97-billion-earth-2050-growth-rate-slowing-says-new-un-population-report

[8] Nigam SN, Chaudhari S, Deevi KC, Saxena KB, Janila P. Trends in legume production and future outlook. In: Saxena KB, Saxena RK, Varshney RK, editors. Genetic Enhancement in Major Food Legumes: Advances in Major Food Legumes. Cham, Switzerland: Springer International Publishing; 2021. p. 7–48

[9] Hughes J, Pearson E, Grafenauer S. Legumes-a comprehensive exploration of global food-based dietary guidelines and consumption. Nutrients. 2022;**14** (15):3080

[10] Jimenez-Lopez JC, Singh KB, Clemente A, Czubinski J, Ochatt S, et al. Editorial: Legumes for global food security-volume II. Frontiers in Plant Science. 2023;**14**:1273600

[11] Jimenez-Lopez JC, Singh KB, Clemente A, Nelson MN, Ochatt S, Smith PMC. Editorial: Legumes for global food security. Frontiers in Plant Science. 2020;**11**:926

[12] Yanni AE, Iakovidi S, Vasilikopoulou E, Karathanos VT. Legumes: A vehicle for transition to sustainability. Nutrients. 2023;**16**(1):98

[13] Cusworth G, Garnett T, Lorimer J. Legume dreams: The contested futures of sustainable plant-based food systems in Europe. Global Environmental Change. 2021;**69**:102321

[14] Hall C, Hillen C, Garden Robinson J. Composition, nutritional value, and health benefits of pulses. Cereal Chemistry. 2017;**94**(1):11–31

[15] Semba RD, Ramsing R, Rahman N, Kraemer K, Bloem MW. Legumes as a sustainable source of protein in human

diets. Global Food Security. 2021;**28**:100520

[16] Akchaya K, Parasuraman P, Pandian K, Vijayakumar S, Thirukumaran K, Mustaffa MRAF, et al. Boosting resource use efficiency, soil fertility, food security, ecosystem services, and climate resilience with legume intercropping: A review. Frontiers in Sustainable Food Systems. 2025;**9**:1527256

[17] Islam MA, Sarkar D, Alam MR, Jahangir MMR, Ali MO, et al. Legumes in conservation agriculture: A sustainable approach in rice-based ecology of the Eastern Indo-Gangetic Plain of South Asia-an overview. Technology in Agronomy 2023;**3**:1–17

[18] Gulia V, Singh Dhull S, Beniwal D, Deepali D, Sangwan A, Rani J. Legumes and their role in linking nutrition, sustainability and veganism. International Journal of Vegetable Science. 2025;**31**(4):593–611

[19] Kumawat A, Bamboriya SD, Meena RS, Yadav D, Kumar A, et al. Legume-based inter-cropping to achieve the crop, soil, and environmental health security. In: Meena RS, Kumar S, editors. Advances in Legumes for Sustainable Intensification. United States: Academic Press; 2022. p. 307–328

[20] Odeku OA, Ogunniyi QA, Ogbole OO, Fettke J. Forgotten gems: Exploring the untapped benefits of underutilized legumes in agriculture, nutrition, and environmental sustainability. Plants. 2024;**13**(9):1208

[21] Basheer-Salimia R, Aloweidat MY, Al-Salimiya MA, Hamdan YAS, Sayara TAS. Comparative study of five legume species under drought conditions. Legume Research: An International Journal. 2021;**44**(6)712–717

[22] Li Y, Hossain MS, Libault M. Single-cell omics in legumes: Research trends and applications. Plants (Basel, Switzerland). 2025;**14**(23):3615

[23] Rashvand M, Nikzadfar M, Laveglia S, Bozorgi A, Paterna G, et al. Advancing legume quality assessment through machine learning: Current trends and future directions. Journal of Food Composition and Analysis. 2025;**142**:107532

[24] Sharma N, Kumar R, Singh AP, Sharma R, Sharma P, et al. Legumes in cropping system for soil ecosystem improvement: A review. Legume Research 2025;**48**:1–9

Chapter 2

Legumes: Nutritional, Health, Agricultural and Environmental Benefits and Cultivation Practices

Sate Sahle

Abstract

Legumes, belonging to the Fabaceae (Leguminosae) family, represent one of the most agronomically and nutritionally important crop groups worldwide. They provide high-quality plant protein, dietary fiber, essential micronutrients, and bioactive compounds that contribute significantly to human health and global food security. Beyond their nutritional importance, legumes play a pivotal role in sustainable agriculture due to their ability to biologically fix atmospheric nitrogen through symbiosis with Rhizobium species, thereby improving soil fertility and reducing reliance on synthetic nitrogen fertilizers. This chapter reviews the nutritional and health benefits of legumes, their agricultural and environmental contributions, cultivation and production practices, and their economic and food security applications. Special emphasis is placed on the future role of legumes in sustainable intensification, climate change mitigation, carbon sequestration, and resilience of farming systems. The integration of legumes into diversified cropping systems is presented as a strategic pathway toward achieving climate-smart agriculture and global sustainability goals.

Keywords: legumes, pulses, biological nitrogen fixation, sustainable agriculture, climate change mitigation, soil fertility, food security, carbon sequestration

1. Introduction

Legumes are a diverse group of flowering plants classified within the family Fabaceae, one of the largest plant families globally [1]. They are characterized by pod-bearing fruits and the capacity to form symbiotic relationships with nitrogen-fixing bacteria in root nodules [2]. Major legume crops include Glycine max, Phaseolus vulgaris, Cicer arietinum, Lens culinaris, and Vigna unguiculata [1, 3]. Pulses refer specifically to the dry, edible seeds of leguminous crops, excluding those harvested green or used for oil extraction [4]. Legumes serve multiple roles as food crops, forage, green manure, and soil-improving components in agricultural systems [2, 5].

2. Nutritional and health benefits of legumes

Legumes are nutrient-dense foods rich in plant protein (18%–30%), complex carbohydrates, dietary fiber, vitamins, and minerals [3]. They complement cereals by supplying lysine, an essential amino acid typically limited in cereal grains, thereby improving overall protein quality (**Table 1**) [6].

Legumes enhance glycemic control due to their low glycemic index (GI range: 10–40, depending on the species) and high resistant starch content [7]. They provide essential micronutrients such as iron (3–8 mg/100 g), zinc (2–5 mg/100 g), magnesium (120–190 mg/100 g), and folate (150–350 μg/100 g) [8]. Regular consumption has been associated with reduced risks of cardiovascular diseases (≈10%–14% risk reduction), obesity (lower BMI and improved satiety markers), colorectal cancer (≈8% lower risk), and type 2 diabetes (≈20%–35% lower incidence in cohort studies) [9–11] (**Figure 1**).

3. Agricultural and environmental benefits

Legumes contribute to agricultural sustainability through biological nitrogen fixation (BNF), improving soil fertility and reducing dependence on synthetic nitrogen fertilizers [2]. Depending on the species and environmental conditions, legumes can fix between **30 and 300 kg N ha^{-1} year^{-1}**, significantly lowering fertilizer requirements [12]. They enhance soil organic matter through root biomass and residue incorporation, improve soil aggregation and structure, stimulate microbial diversity, and increase nutrient cycling efficiency (**Table 2**) [13].

Legume	Protein (%)	Dietary fiber (%)	Iron (mg)	Zinc (mg)	Folate (μg)	Glycemic index
Soybean	36–40	9–15	15.7	4.9	375	16
Lentil	24–26	10–12	6.5–7.5	3.3	180	21–29
Chickpea	19–21	12–17	4.3–6.2	2.5–3.5	172	28–36
Common bean	21–23	15–25	5.0–8.2	2.8–3.5	130–230	24–40
Cowpea	23–25	10–11	4.5–8.0	2.7–4.0	200	33

Source: Compiled from FAO food composition databases and peer-reviewed nutrition studies [3, 6–8].

Table 1.
Nutritional composition of selected legumes (per 100 g dry weight).

Conceptual summary based on meta-analyses:

- ↓ LDL cholesterol: 5–10% reduction
- ↓ Cardiovascular disease risk: 10–14%
- ↓ Type 2 diabetes risk: 20–35%
- ↓ Colorectal cancer risk: ~8%
- Improved satiety and weight control markers

Figure 1.
Health Impact of Regular Legume consumption. Source: Synthesized from epidemiological and clinical studies [9–11].

Parameter	Reported range	Example/Impact	Reference
Biological nitrogen fixation	30–300 kg N ha^{-1} yr^{-1}	Soybean ≈ 50–200 kg N ha^{-1}	[2, 12]
Residual N benefit to cereals	20–80 kg N ha^{-1}	Wheat yield increases 10%–35%	[14]
Soil organic carbon increases	0.1–0.4 t C ha^{-1} yr^{-1}	Improved aggregate stability	[13]
Nitrate leaching reduction	30%–50%	Compared to fertilized monocropping	[16]
N_2O emission reduction	15%–45%	Lower than synthetic N systems	[15]

Source: Synthesized from long-term field experiments and meta-analyses [2, 12–16].

Table 2.
Empirical data on agricultural and environmental benefits of legumes.

Conceptual quantitative summary from experimental studies:

- Biological nitrogen fixation: up to 300 kg N ha^{-1}
- Reduced synthetic fertilizer use: 20–100% depending on system
- Soil carbon sequestration: 0.1–0.4 t C ha^{-1} yr^{-1}
- Nitrate leaching reduction: up to 50%
- N_2O emission reduction: up to 45%

These ecosystem services contribute directly to climate change mitigation and sustainable intensification.

Figure 2.
Environmental pathways of legume-based systems. These ecosystem services contribute directly to climate change mitigation and sustainable intensification.Source: Based on global field studies and meta-analyses [2, 12–16].

Legume–cereal rotations improve yields of subsequent crops, often resulting in **10%–35% yield increases** in cereals due to residual nitrogen effects [14]. Furthermore, replacing synthetic nitrogen fertilizers with legume-derived nitrogen reduces environmental pollution by minimizing nitrate leaching (up to a 30%–50% reduction) and nitrous oxide (N_2O) emissions, a potent greenhouse gas [15, 16] (**Figure 2**).

4. Cultivation and production practices

Successful legume production requires the selection of high-yielding and climate-adapted varieties, proper land preparation, seed inoculation with effective Rhizobium strains, balanced nutrient management (especially phosphorus), integrated pest management (IPM), efficient water management, and appropriate harvesting and storage practices [3].

Inoculation with effective Rhizobium strains can increase grain yield by **10%–30%** and enhance nitrogen fixation by **20–60 kg N ha^{-1}** compared with non-inoculated crops [17]. Adequate phosphorus fertilization (20–60 kg P_2O_5 ha^{-1} depending on soil status) significantly improves nodulation, root development, and yield, with reported yield increases of **15%–40%** in deficient soils [18] (**Table 3**).

Agronomic practice	Quantitative impact	Example outcome	Reference
Rhizobium inoculation	10%–30% yield increase	+0.3–0.8 t ha^{-1} grain	[17]
Nitrogen fixation enhancement	+20–60 kg N ha^{-1}	Reduced fertilizer need	[17]
Phosphorus fertilization (20–60 kg P_2O_5 ha^{-1})	15%–40% yield increase	Improved nodulation	[18]
IPM implementation	15%–25% loss reduction	30–50% lower pesticide use	[19]
Supplemental irrigation	20%–35% yield increase	Improved pod filling	[20]
Improved storage (10%–12% moisture)	20%–40% reduction in post-harvest loss	Reduced insect damage	[21]

Source: Synthesized from field trials and agronomic meta-analyses [3, 17–21].

Table 3.
Empirical effects of agronomic practices on legume productivity.

Integrated productivity gains from management improvements:

- Variety selection: +10–25% yield advantage
- Rhizobium inoculation: +10–30%
- Phosphorus management: +15–40%
- Irrigation optimization: +20–35%
- IPM adoption: Reduced yield loss by up to 25%
- Improved storage: Reduced post-harvest loss by up to 40%

Cumulatively, integrated management can double productivity in low-input systems while reducing environmental impacts.

Figure 3.
Contribution of improved agronomic practices to sustainable legume production. Cumulatively, integrated management can double productivity in low-input systems while reducing environmental impacts. Source: Based on multi-location trials and FAO technical guidelines [3, 17–21].

IPM strategies can reduce yield losses (commonly 15%–25% under pest pressure) while lowering pesticide use by up to **30%–50%** [19]. Efficient water management, particularly supplemental irrigation during flowering and pod filling, may improve yields by **20%–35%** in semi-arid conditions [20]. Collectively, improved agronomic management enhances productivity while maintaining environmental sustainability through optimized input use and a reduced ecological footprint [21] (**Figure 3**).

5. Economic and food security applications

Legumes contribute significantly to household income, employment generation, livestock feed systems, and export earnings, particularly in developing countries [22]. In many sub-Saharan African countries, grain legumes account for **10%–20% of smallholder farm income**, and in some export-oriented systems (e.g., common beans and chickpeas), they generate substantial foreign exchange earnings [23] (**Table 4**).

Indicator	Empirical data	Impact	Reference
Contribution to smallholder income	10%–20% of annual farm income	Income diversification	[28]
Export earnings (selected countries)	USD 500 million annually (major pulse exporters)	Foreign exchange generation	[22]
Crude protein in legume residues	12%–25%	Improved livestock productivity	[24]
Storage life (properly dried, 10%–12% moisture).	6–12 months	Reduced seasonal food shortages	[25]
Yield stability under drought	10%–30% less yield loss compared to cereals	Enhanced food system stability	[26]

Source: Compiled from FAO statistics, World Bank reports, and peer-reviewed agricultural economics studies [22, 24–28].

Table 4.
Economic and Food Security Contributions of Legumes.

Legume residues and by-products serve as high-protein livestock feed (12%–25% crude protein), improving milk yield and animal growth performance [24]. Their affordability and long shelf-life (6–12 months under proper storage) enhance food availability and accessibility, especially during lean seasons [25]. Legumes support the four pillars of food security – availability, access, utilization, and stability – by increasing domestic production, diversifying diets, improving nutrient intake, and stabilizing food systems under climatic and market variability [26, 27] (**Figure 4**).

Availability

- Increased domestic pulse production (global production >95 million tons annually)
- Yield stability under marginal conditions

Access

- Lower market price per unit protein compared to animal sources
- Income generation for smallholders

Utilization

- 18–30% protein content
- High micronutrient density

Stability

- Drought tolerance
- Long storage life (6–12 months)
- Reduced dependence on imported fertilizers

Figure 4.
Role of legumes in the Four Pillars of Food security. Source: Synthesized from global food security and agricultural economic analyses [22, 24–28].

Benefit category	Measured effect	Source
Soil Organic Carbon (SOC) increases	Up to ~ 29.6 % increase in SOC fractions vs. non-legumes	[31]
BNF Reduces Synthetic N Need	Up to 40 % reduction in fertilizer dependency	[31]
GWP Reduction in Rotations	~9 % lower GWP in legume-integrated systems vs. conventional	[32]
N_2O Emission Reduction	Legume inclusion can lower N_2O emissions (e.g., pea: 69 vs. wheat: 368 kg N_2O ha^{-1})	[30]

Notes: – SOC = Soil Organic Carbon
– GWP = Global Warming Potential
– N_2O = Nitrous oxide emissions.

Table 5.
Quantified benefits of legumes in climate-smart agriculture.

6. Future role of legumes in sustainable agriculture and climate change mitigation

Integrating legumes into cropping systems represents a strategic intervention for reducing external nitrogen inputs while enhancing agroecosystem resilience under changing climatic conditions [29]. Through BNF, legumes convert atmospheric N_2 into plant-usable nitrogen, lowering the need for synthetic nitrogen fertilizer – which is energy-intensive to produce and a major source of nitrous oxide emissions – thus contributing to greenhouse gas mitigation [30].

Incorporating legumes into cropping systems can also increase soil organic carbon (SOC) stocks; for example, legumes have been shown to enhance SOC through root biomass and microbial activity, with estimates of SOC increases up to ~ 29.6 % relative to other systems and deep root effects that stabilize carbon in the soil profile [31]. Experimental field trials have documented that legume-based rotations can reduce the global warming potential (GWP) of cropping systems (e.g., reductions of ~ 9 % GWP compared to conventional wheat–maize systems) while also improving subsequent crop yields through improved soil fertility [32]. Future priorities include breeding climate-resilient legume varieties with enhanced nitrogen fixation efficiency, strengthening value chains for legumes to improve adoption and market access, and integrating legume strategies into national climate adaptation and mitigation plans to scale their benefits across broader agroecosystems [31, 30] (**Table 5**).

7. Conclusion

Legumes represent cornerstone crops for sustainable food systems. Their nutritional richness addresses malnutrition and chronic diseases, while their agronomic benefits enhance soil fertility, reduce fertilizer dependence, and lower greenhouse gas emissions. Expanding legume-based systems is essential for achieving global food security, environmental sustainability, and climate change mitigation goals.

Acknowledgments

The author acknowledges the use of an AI tool for language polishing and an AI tool for figure creation in the manuscript.

Author details

Sate Sahle
Department of Plant Sciences, Wachemo University, Hossana, Ethiopia

*Address all correspondence to: seatesahle@email.com

References

[1] Lewis G, Schrire B, Mackinder B, Lock M. Legumes of the World. UK: Royal Botanic Gardens, Kew; 2005

[2] Giller KE. Nitrogen Fixation in Tropical Cropping Systems. Wallingford, UK: CABI; 2001

[3] FAO. Food Composition Table for Pulses and Legumes. Rome: FAO; 2019

[4] FAO. Pulses and Their By-products as Animal Feed. Rome: FAO; 2016

[5] Peoples MB, Herridge MJ, Ladha JK. The contributions of nitrogen-fixing crop legumes to agricultural sustainability. Plant and Soil. 2009;**315**:1–18

[6] Young VR, Pellett PL. Plant proteins in relation to human protein and amino acid nutrition. American Journal of Clinical Nutrition. 1994;**59**:1203S–1212S

[7] Mudryj AN, Yu N, Aukema HM. Nutritional and health benefits of pulses. Applied Physiology, Nutrition, and Metabolism. 2014;**39**:1197–1204

[8] Gibson RS. Principles of Nutritional Assessment. Oxford, 2nd ed. UK: Oxford University Press; 2005

[9] Gibson RS. Principles of nutritional assessment. 2nd ed. Oxford University Press; 2005

[10] Bazzano LA, Jiang H, Lorena OG, Catherine LM, Paul WK. Legume consumption and risk of coronary heart disease. Archives of Internal Medicine. 2001;**161**:2573–2578

[11] Viguiliouk E, Kendall CWC, Blanco Mejia S, Cozma AI, Ha V, Mirrahimi A, Jayalath VH, Augustin LSA, Chiavaroli L, Leiter LA, de Souza RJ, Jenkins DJA, Sievenpiper JL. Effect of Tree Nuts on Glycemic Control in Diabetes: A Systematic Review and Meta-Analysis of Randomized Controlled Dietary Trials. PLoS ONE. 2014;**9**(7):e103376. DOI: 10.1371/journal.pone.0103376

[12] Peoples MB, Herridge DF, Ladha JK. Biological nitrogen fixation: An efficient source of nitrogen for sustainable agricultural production? Plant and Soil. 1995;**174**:3–28

[13] Drinkwater LE, Wagoner P, Sarrantonio M. Legume-based cropping systems have reduced carbon and nitrogen losses. Nature. 1998; **396**:262–265

[14] Preissel S, Reckling M, Schläfke N, Zander P. Magnitude and farm-economic value of grain legume pre-crop benefits in Europe. Field Crops Research. 2015;**1**(75):64–79

[15] IPCC. Climate Change 2022: Mitigation of Climate Change. Cambridge, UK: Cambridge University Press; 2022

[16] Tonitto C, David MB, Drinkwater LE. Replacing bare fallows with cover crops in fertilizer-intensive cropping systems: A meta-analysis. Agriculture, Ecosystems & Environment. 2006;**112**:58–72

[17] Herridge DF, Peoples MB, Boddey RM. Global inputs of biological nitrogen fixation in agricultural systems. Plant and Soil. 2008;**311**:1–18

[18] Sanginga N, Woomer PL. Integrated Soil Fertility Management in Africa. Nairobi, Kenya: CAB International; 2009

[19] Pretty J, Bharucha ZP. Integrated pest management for sustainable intensification. Insects. 2015;**6**:152–182

[20] Rockström J, Falkenmark M. Agriculture: Increase water harvesting in Africa. Nature. 2015;**519**:283–285

[21] Affognon HD, Crispin M, Pascal S, Christiannon B. Post-harvest losses in sub-Saharan Africa: A meta-analysis. World Development. 2015;**66**:49–68

[22] FAO. FAOSTAT Statistical Database. Rome: FAO; 2023

[23] Rockström J, Falkenmark M. Agriculture: Increase water harvesting in Africa. Nature. 2015;**519**(7543): 283–285. DOI: 10.1038/519283a

[24] Singh BB, Ajeigbe HA, Tarawali SA. Improving the production and utilization of cowpea as food and fodder. Field Crops Research. 2003;**84**:169–177

[25] Hodges RJ, et al. Postharvest losses and waste in developed and less developed countries. Journal of Stored Products Research. 2011;**47**:89–97

[26] International Institute of Tropical Agriculture (IITA). Grain legumes for livelihood improvement. International Institute of Tropical Agriculture; 2018. Available from: https://www.iita.org/

[27] Singh BB, Ajeigbe HA, Tarawali SA. Improving the production and utilization of cowpea as food and fodder. Field Crops Research. 2003;**84**(1–2):169–177. DOI: 10.1016/S0378-4290(03)00148-5

[28] Hodges RJ, Buzby JC, Bennett B. Postharvest losses and waste in developed and less developed countries: Opportunities to improve resource use. The Journal of Agricultural Science. 2011;**149**(S1):37–45. DOI: 10.1017/S0021859610000936

[29] High Level Panel of Experts on Food Security and Nutrition (HLPE). Food security and nutrition: Building a global narrative. High Level Panel of Experts on Food Security and Nutrition. 2020. Available from: https://openknowledge.fao.org/server/api/core/bitstreams/8357b6eb-8010-4254-814a-1493faaf4a93/content

[30] International Fund for Agricultural Development (IFAD). Rural development report 2016: Fostering inclusive rural transformation. International Fund for Agricultural Development. 2016. Available from: https://www.ifad.org/en/w/publications/rural-development-report-2016

[31] Lin F, Liu Y, Zhang L, Zhang Y. Legume-Based rotations enhance ecosystem sustainability in the North China Plain: Trade-Offs between greenhouse gas mitigation, soil carbon sequestration, and economic viability. Agriculture. 2026;**16**(1):116. DOI: 10.3390/agriculture16010116

[32] Lötjönen S, Ollikainen M. Does crop rotation with legumes provide an efficient means to reduce nutrient loads and GHG emissions? Review of Agricultural, Food and Environmental Studies. 2018;**98**:283–312

Chapter 3

Potential of Legume Landraces to Combat Hidden Hunger

Elisa Gorbe, Irene Moreno-Valle and Consuelo Penella

Abstract

Hidden hunger (or micronutrient malnutrition) affects over two billion people globally and is not limited to low-income countries. It is also known to impact populations in high and middle-income nations due to dietary shifts towards ultra-processed foods. Legumes (Fabaceae/Leguminosae family) represent an affordable and sustainable solution to this problem, as they are rich in protein, fiber, and essential minerals such as Fe, Zn, and Mg. However, in recent decades, breeding activities have focused exclusively on legume yield, which has led to a dilution effect that reduces mineral density and disrupts symbiotic relationships with soil microbiota, leaving the nutritional potential of most commercial legume varieties compromised. This chapter critically examines the multifactorial causes of low nutrient density in modern legumes, moving beyond the popular narrative of soil depletion to highlight the roles of varietal selection, microbial degradation, and agronomic practices. It also explores the untapped potential of legume landraces – genetically diverse, locally adapted traditional varieties – as reservoirs of superior nutritional quality and genetic traits for biofortification. The chapter further evaluates the applications of landraces across multiple domains: as raw materials for functional foods and nutraceuticals, as high-value ingredients in health-conscious markets, as mineral-dense components in sustainable livestock systems, and as key elements in agroecological restoration. In conclusion, the conservation and strategic use of legume landraces, combined with agroecological practices, offer a viable pathway to simultaneously combat hidden hunger, restore soil health, and build more resilient and nutritious food systems.

Keywords: hidden hunger, landraces, legumes, micronutrients, biofortification, functional foods, soil microbiota, dilution effect, sustainable agriculture

1. Introduction

The total number of people going hungry has been increasing. Almost 690 million people were undernourished in 2019, an increase of 60 million people since 2014 [1]. Within this global situation, the 2030 Sustainable Development Goals established '*ending hunger, achieving food security and improved nutrition, and promoting sustainable agriculture*' as Goal 2 [1]. This global goal involves a broad definition of hunger, including calorie deficiencies (chronic hunger), micronutrient deficiencies (hidden hunger), and related health problems [2].

Hidden hunger is defined as the presence of multiple micronutrient deficiencies in the absence of an energy-deficit diet [3]. Micronutrients, including vitamins and minerals, are required in very small but specific amounts by the human body and are essential for people's well-being and health. It is estimated that more than two billion people are affected by hidden hunger [2], though this number may be even higher as most micronutrient deficiencies remain undiagnosed due to non-specific symptoms [4]. Hidden hunger affects high-, middle-, and low-income countries [4–6]. Fe, Zn, I, and vitamin A are the most common limiting micronutrients in the diet, deficiencies that often occur because of consuming an energy-dense but nutrient-poor diet [3]. In this global context, legumes present themselves as an affordable, sustainable, and micronutrient-rich solution to combat hidden hunger. They provide micronutrient density – including Ca, K, Mg, P, Fe, and Zn [7] – often missing in a cereal-based diet. India produces 26.2% of global pulses, followed by Canada, the European Union, Australia, and China, each accounting for 5%–6% of global production [8].

Legumes (Fabaceae/Leguminosae family) constitute a fundamental pillar in sustainable agriculture, as they have a unique ability to fix atmospheric nitrogen into the soil due to symbiosis with *Rhizobium* bacteria. Legumes can contribute 100–300 kg of N per hectare [9]. This fixation reduces reliance on external fertilizers and improves the nutrient balance of the soil. Additionally, the use of legumes as green manure acts as a carbon sink and enhances the soil's physical and biological properties [10]. Recognising these systemic benefits, the European Union's Common Agricultural Policy (CAP) framework explicitly promotes legume cultivation as a key practice for carbon farming, aiming to sequester carbon in soils and biomass [11]. Consequently, institutions like OECD/FAO [12] emphasise that integrating these species into cropping systems is an essential tool for regenerative agriculture, capable of restoring the health of degraded soils while contributing to climate mitigation.

Historically, legume breeding has prioritised yield over nutritional quality, leading to a 'dilution effect', where increased yields and plant dry matter are inversely correlated with mineral concentration [13]. This decline is exacerbated by mineral fertilization. Consequently, commercial varieties often exhibit lower levels of key micronutrients and vitamins compared to their genetic predecessors [14]. As the Green Revolution intensified this focus on yield, the cultivation of landraces sharply declined, resulting in significant genetic erosion [15, 16]. This loss is particularly critical because landraces have consistently been shown to possess a higher micronutrient content than modern cultivars [15].

In this context, the conservation and use of legume landraces emerge as a key nutritional resource to address hidden hunger. Given that mineral deficiencies are central to this form of malnutrition, this chapter will focus on these critical nutrients. Therefore, this chapter aims to critically analyse the causes of low nutrient density in legumes and to evaluate the potential of landraces and agroecological practices as strategies to enhance their nutritional value in sustainable food systems.

2. The real causes of low nutrient density: Beyond soil depletion

Popular opinion, echoed by integrative health discourse, holds that the decrease in micronutrient contents in plants is directly related to depleted soils.

This perspective argues that modern intensive agriculture has broken the traditional nutrient cycle, where organic matter returned to the soil, and that the use of synthetic fertilizers, focused on N, P, and K while neglecting others like Mg, has led to imbalances and soil exhaustion [17, 18].

Restoring soil health is, therefore, crucial for sustainable agriculture and long-term fertility, but the relationship between soil mineral content and the nutritional quality of harvested crops is more complex than often assumed. Several studies have found no conclusive evidence that directly corroborates soil mineral content as the sole determinant of nutrient density in harvested crops [19–21]. In fact, research indicates that a primary driver for reduced nutrient concentration may be the selection of modern cultivars for higher yield, which can lead to a dilution effect, as previously stated [13]. To directly address this dilution effect, the mineral concentration of legumes can be enhanced through biofortification. Biofortification methods include integrated nutrient management, the addition of soil microorganisms (such as mycorrhizal fungi and nitrogen-fixing bacteria), intercropping legumes with cereals, and crop breeding for higher vitamin and mineral content [20].

Microbial diversity of the rhizosphere also plays an important role in micronutrient availability [22], ultimately affecting the final composition of food products. The availability of essential micronutrients in the rhizosphere is fundamentally governed by microbial activity rather than simple mineral abundance. Soil microorganisms serve as indispensable mediators that transform insoluble trace elements into plant-available forms through diverse biochemical mechanisms. For instance, the secretion of high-affinity Fe-chelating compounds, known as siderophores, is critical for overcoming iron scarcity in alkaline soils [23]. Furthermore, specialised bacteria and arbuscular mycorrhizal fungi (AMF) enhance the uptake of Zn, Cu, and Mn by secreting organic acids that lower localised pH and by extending the physical reach of the root system [24]. Consequently, intensive agricultural practices that lead to the biological degradation of the soil directly undermine these vital communities [25], compromising micronutrient concentrations in legumes cultivated under such conditions.

Intensive management exerts this detrimental effect through multiple pathways. For example, synthetic fertilizers directly impair soil microorganisms. As demonstrated by Treseder [26], nitrogen (N) fertilization suppresses microbial growth by altering soil chemistry. Specifically, ionic accumulation can create toxic osmotic stress, while nitrogen-induced acidification leads to aluminum (Al) mobilisation and the leaching of essential nutrients like magnesium (Mg) and calcium (Ca) [26]. These combined stressors – Al-toxicity, osmotic imbalance, and nutrient limitation – fundamentally constrain microbial communities [26]. Similarly, AMF are particularly affected by the external inputs of N and phosphorus (P). As stated by Verbruggen and Toby [27], when exposed to high nutrient concentrations, host plants may severely decrease or cease resource allocation to their fungal partners, resulting in decreased AMF colonisation. Consequently, fertilized fields show a decline in mutualistic, nutrient-transferring arbuscular forms in favor of vesicle-forming morphotypes – structures associated with resource storage and a more parasitic strategy [27].

The application of synthetic pesticides and herbicides also represents a significant chemical stressor that reshapes the functional and taxonomic composition of soil microbiota. Chronic exposure to these agrochemicals can lead to a reduction in microbial enzymatic activities, which are vital for nutrient mineralisation [28]. This selective pressure often diminishes microbial richness, favouring the proliferation of species that can metabolise the chemicals and suppressing sensitive, beneficial taxa [29]. Beyond chemical inputs, physical practices like tillage are equally disruptive. Tillage is known to accelerate the mineralisation of soil organic matter, leading to a rapid depletion of the primary carbon sources that sustain microbiota [30]. Furthermore, the mechanical disruption of the soil profile has a direct effect on AMF [31]. Collectively, these findings underscore that enhancing soil microbial communities through agroecological practices is fundamental for improving micronutrient concentrations in legumes.

3. Comparative analysis of mineral diversity: Unlocking the nutritional potential of legume landraces

To evaluate the nutritional divergence between traditional and modern legumes, **Table 1** synthesises mineral concentration data from international studies across multiple pulse species: lentils (*Lens culinaris* Medik.), faba beans (*Vicia faba* L.), chickpeas (*Cicer arietinum* L.), common beans (*Phaseolus vulgaris* L.), peas (*Pisum sativum* L.), Bambara groundnuts (*Vigna subterranea* (L.) Verdc.), pigeon peas (*Cajanus cajan* (L.) Millsp.), soybeans (*Glycine max* (L.) Merr.), and cowpeas (*Vigna unguiculata* (L.) Walp.).

To compile this dataset, a comprehensive literature search following predefined criteria was conducted. Peer-reviewed studies reporting original mineral concentrations for the target species were identified through searches in databases including Science Direct and Google Scholar, as well as in the AI-powered academic search engine Elicit, using keyword combinations that included generic terms such as 'micronutrient legume landraces' and 'legume mineral composition', as well as more specific queries that combined target elements (e.g., iron, zinc, magnesium), species (using both scientific and common names, for example, *Phaseolus vulgaris* or common bean, *Cicer arietinum* or chickpea), genotypes (with terms such as 'landraces' or 'commercial' either included or omitted to broaden the search), and geographical locations (e.g., Turkey, Africa, America), which could be included or omitted as needed. Representative examples include 'Magnesium soybean landraces', 'Iron chickpea landraces', 'Zinc legume landraces Africa', and "Phaseolus vulgaris selenium Turkey."

Studies were included if they: (i) provided quantitative data on at least one target mineral (Fe, Zn, Mg, K, Cu, Mn, B, Mo, Ni, Se, I) in seeds; (ii) clearly distinguished between landraces, commercial cultivars, or germplasm accessions (studies comparing landraces and commercial varieties were prioritised, but those reporting data for only one group were also considered); and (iii) were published in peer-reviewed journals or by recognised research institutions. Data were manually extracted from tables and text, and all concentrations were standardised to uniform units (mg kg^{-1} for most elements; g kg^{-1} for Mg and K) to ensure comparability. Due to heterogeneity in experimental conditions, geographic origins, and analytical methods, the analysis is primarily descriptive and comparative, focusing on the range (minimum–maximum) and mean values for each seed type rather than a formal meta-analysis. This approach highlights the broad genetic diversity within legume germplasm.

The dataset integrates findings from research conducted in primary centers of biodiversity and regions with deep-rooted legume cultivation traditions, including

Author	Scientific name	Type	n	Fe mg kg^{-1}			Zn mg kg^{-1}			Se mg kg^{-1}			I mg kg^{-1}			Mg g kg^{-1}			K g kg^{-1}			Cu mg kg^{-1}			Mn mg kg^{-1}			B mg kg^{-1}			Mo mg kg^{-1}			Ni mg kg^{-1}		
				min	max	mean	min	max	mean	min	max	mean	min	max	mean	min	max	mean	min	max	mean	min	max	mean	min	max	mean	min	max	mean	min	max	mean	min	max	mean
[40]	*Phaseolus vulgaris* L.	L	10	50.1	117.4	71.3	36.5	60.5	44.4	0.0	0.0	0.0	-	-	-	1.1	1.7	1.4	14.5	18.1	15.8	1.9	5.1	3.3	15.2	27.2	20.1	1.1	4.2	2.8	3.7	37.3	13.0	0.0	0.4	0.2
[42]		L	26	19.0	35.9	27.7	19.3	33.0	23.4	-	-	-	-	-	-	0.2	0.4	0.3	11.7	14.0	12.8	7.5	12.3	9.2	11.2	25.9	16.0	-	-	-	-	-	-	-	-	-
[49]		L	23	46.0	116.0	74.1	22.0	54.0	38.4	-	-	-	-	-	-	1.6	2.5	2.0	13.0	20.6	16.1	8.0	14.0	10.2	10.0	19.0	13.2	12.0	26.0	17.0	-	-	-	-	-	-
[46]		L	20	32.1	158.9	33.9	2.4	96.5	33.9	0.0	6.0	0.6	-	-	-	1.7	2.7	2.1	14.2	26.3	18.5	6.2	26.8	11.6	12.9	43.9	24.3	-	-	-	0.6	5.7	1.9	0.0	9.8	2.8
[15]		L	10	-	115.1	-	17.8	37.9	-	-	0.5	-	-	-	-	-	-	-	-	-	-	-	-	-	-	-	-	-	-	-	-	-	-	-	-	-
[39]		C	1	65.5	82.7	74.4	32.5	39.4	35.4	0.0	0.0	0.0	-	-	-	0.0	0.0	1.4	0.0	0.0	14.3	2.2	2.9	2.4	17.5	18.8	18.2	2.2	4.0	3.3	6.7	10.1	8.1	0.0	0.0	0.0
[42]		C	27	41.6	17.5	35.1	19.5	33.9	28.8	-	-	-	-	-	-	0.3	0.5	0.4	11.3	14.9	13.4	9.2	12.5	11.2	13.9	31.5	22.2	-	-	-	-	-	-	-	-	-
[49]		C	5	51.0	73.0	60.9	32.0	42.0	37.0	-	-	-	-	-	-	1.9	2.4	2.1	14.3	17.5	16.2	8.0	14.0	10.4	11.0	19.0	13.7	14.0	29.0	19.0	-	-	-	-	-	-
[50]		C	8	53.0	69.0	59.0	24.0	32.0	28.1	-	-	-	-	-	-	1.7	2.3	1.9	15.4	16.9	16.3	-	-	-	14.0	29.0	19.8	10.1	13.3	12.0	-	-	-	-	-	-
[51]		C	3	41.0	82.0	59.3	18.1	38.8	25.4	-	-	-	-	-	-	-	-	-	-	-	-	-	-	-	-	-	-	-	-	-	-	-	-	-	-	-
[34]		C	-	-	-	-	-	-	-	-	-	-	0.1	0.1	0.1	-	-	-	-	-	-	-	-	-	-	-	-	-	-	-	-	-	-	-	-	-
[52]		C	25	24.8	57.5	42.8	27.1	41.3	32.5	-	-	-	-	-	-	-	-	-	-	-	-	-	-	-	-	-	-	-	-	-	-	-	-	-	-	-
[46]		C	5	32.1	158.9	80.2	10.4	64.6	27.9	0.8	4.7	2.1	-	-	-	1.6	2.8	2.0	14.1	22.6	18.5	6.7	17.2	11.2	18.2	41.3	25.9	-	-	-	0.8	4.7	1.9	1.2	5.7	2.9
[15]		C	5	-	133.6	-	25.0	35.1	-	-	-	-	-	-	-	-	-	-	-	-	-	-	-	-	-	-	-	-	-	-	-	-	-	-	-	-
[53]		G	380	-	-	53.4	-	-	35.8	-	-	-	-	-	-	-	-	-	-	-	-	-	-	-	-	-	-	-	-	-	-	-	-	-	-	-
		G	215	-	-	55.5	-	-	34.4	-	-	-	-	-	-	-	-	-	-	-	-	-	-	-	-	-	-	-	-	-	-	-	-	-	-	-
		G	38	-	-	59.1	-	-	35.9	-	-	-	-	-	-	-	-	-	-	-	-	-	-	-	-	-	-	-	-	-	-	-	-	-	-	-
		G	439	-	-	55.6	-	-	32.9	-	-	-	-	-	-	-	-	-	-	-	-	-	-	-	-	-	-	-	-	-	-	-	-	-	-	-
[54]		G	155	32.2	88.4	60.3	11.5	45.3	28.4	-	-	-	-	-	-	1.3	2.5	1.9	12.4	21.2	16.8	4.7	13.5	9.1	8.0	20.1	14.1	-	-	-	-	-	-	-	-	-

Author	Scientific name	Type	n	Fe (mg/kg)			Zn (mg/kg)			Se (mg/kg)			I (mg/kg)			Mg (g/kg)			K (g/kg)			Cu (mg/kg)			Mn (mg/kg)			B (mg/kg)			Mo (mg/kg)			Ni (mg/kg)		
				min	max	mean	min	max	mean	min	max	mean	min	max	mean	min	max	mean	min	max	mean	min	max	mean	min	max	mean	min	max	mean	min	max	mean	min	max	mean
[41, 55]	*Lens culinaris* Medik.	L	39	49.0	81.4	63.6	42.3	73.1	55.0	-	-	-	-	-	-	0.9	1.3	1.1	6.4	9.5	7.5	9.1	16.9	12.1	10.5	16.2	13.4	-	-	-	-	-	-	-	-	-
[37]		L	8	65.7	82.6	76.6	37.4	48.3	41.5	-	-	-	-	-	-	1.0	1.3	1.2	9.2	9.6	9.4	-	-	-	12.7	13.7	13.2	-	-	-	-	-	-	-	-	-
[41, 55]		C	7	49.4	69.9	59.0	46.9	61.3	53.5	-	-	-	-	-	-	0.9	1.2	1.0	6.7	8.4	7.4	9.5	14.5	11.7	11.5	15.4	13.5	-	-	-	-	-	-	-	-	-
[37]		C	-	-	-	73.8	-	-	41.4	-	-	-	-	-	-	-	-	1.1	-	-	9.4	-	-	-	-	-	12.9	-	-	-	-	-	-	-	-	-
[56]		C	34	51.6	72.5	64.8	31.3	38.8	35.5	0.7	1.0	0.8	-	-	-	-	-	1.0	8.4	9.5	9.0	7.2	9.1	7.9	12.2	15.9	13.9	6.6	8.7	7.7	2.0	3.1	2.4	1.7	2.5	2.0
		C		43.1	64.4	57.0	29.4	40.3	36.2	0.6	1.0	0.8	-	-	-	-	-	0.7	8.6	9.9	9.3	6.9	9.0	7.9	10.2	13.2	11.5	5.6	9.2	6.6	2.2	3.1	2.6	2.0	3.0	2.3
[57]		C	6	70.3	96.4	80.6	32.4	40.8	36.2	0.4	0.7	0.5	-	-	-	0.8	0.9	0.9	4.9	5.4	5.1	8.6	11.7	10.4	12.3	16.3	14.1	-	-	-	-	-	-	1.8	2.5	2.1
[58]		G	234	40.5	85.6	66.4	22.4	60.4	45.0	-	-	-	-	-	-	0.7	1.3	1.0	8.6	13.6	10.8	7.5	17.3	12.3	9.3	20.3	13.7	3.6	9.7	5.4	-	-	-	-	-	-
[39]	*Vicia faba* L.	L	13	48.4	108.9	69.1	39.4	66.9	51.1	0.0	0.0	0.0	-	-	-	1.3	2.2	1.8	16.0	23.6	21.0	14.3	18.8	16.2	21.7	30.3	27.1	10.9	16.1	13.0	6.2	38.7	13.4	1.3	3.2	2.2
[38]		L	129	29.7	96.3	59.6	10.4	49.3	24.2	-	-	-	-	-	-	-	-	-	4.5	19.3	13.0	10.3	33.0	18.9	15.5	29.2	23.3	-	-	-	-	-	-	-	-	-
[47]		L	200	44.9	128.5	83.8	28.4	64.3	42.7	-	-	-	-	-	-	3.2	4.2	3.5	9.4	56.0	15.1	8.1	34.2	17.6	16.6	35.8	24.0	-	-	-	-	-	-	-	-	-
[39]		C	1	68.4	73.8	70.1	59.2	63.4	61.1	0.0	0.0	0.0	-	-	-	0.0	0.0	1.6	0.0	0.0	21.7	15.1	16.6	15.8	23.4	25.7	24.5	12.8	14.4	13.6	11.0	11.8	11.3	1.7	2.2	1.9
[38]		C	4	39.4	73.5	59.1	16.6	20.1	18.5	-	-	-	-	-	-	-	-	-	5.9	14.3	11.8	13.9	20.4	18.2	18.0	26.4	23.2	-	-	-	-	-	-	-	-	-
[47]		C	3	69.9	75.3	72.5	36.4	41.6	39.1	-	-	-	-	-	-	3.0	3.1	3.1	16.6	21.3	19.1	19.5	21.5	21.5	22.9	27.7	25.1	-	-	-	-	-	-	-	-	-
[59]		C	6	-	-	-	-	-	-	-	-	-	-	-	-	1.8	2.3	2.0	16.5	18.8	17.8	-	-	-	-	-	-	-	-	-	-	-	-	-	-	-
[60]		C	25	45.0	55.0	50.7	-	-	41.8	-	-	0.2	-	-	-	-	-	1.3	-	-	11.3	-	-	8.2	-	-	14.1	-	-	11.5	-	-	2.4	-	-	3.4
[61]		G	90	59.3	124.1	77.6	36.8	85.7	52.1	-	-	-	-	-	-	1.2	1.8	1.4	10.4	15.8	12.5	7.8	20.5	13.5	11.9	26.5	17.9	9.5	21.4	13.7	-	-	-	-	-	-
[43]	Corrected Text: *Cicer arietinum* L.	L	-	23.0	32.9	26.6	20.6	30.1	24.6	-	-	-	-	-	-	-	-	-	-	-	-	-	-	-	-	-	-	-	-	-	-	-	-	-	-	-
		L	-	31.1	44.2	36.2	17.2	26.9	21.5	-	-	-	-	-	-	-	-	-	-	-	-	-	-	-	-	-	-	-	-	-	-	-	-	-	-	-
		C	-	7.5	52.1	30.4	13.4	38.0	23.6	-	-	-	-	-	-	-	-	-	-	-	-	-	-	-	-	-	-	-	-	-	-	-	-	-	-	-
		C	-	15.5	48.1	32.2	12.3	34.7	22.8	-	-	-	-	-	-	-	-	-	-	-	-	-	-	-	-	-	-	-	-	-	-	-	-	-	-	-
[57]		C	2	49.0	52.1	50.6	29.6	33.7	31.7	0.3	0.4	0.4	-	-	-	-	-	0.9	3.3	4.2	3.8	7.2	8.3	7.8	20.1	22.2	21.2	-	-	-	-	-	-	0.9	1.1	1.0
[62]		C	8	40.3	49.9	46.6	18.8	23.5	20.3	-	-	-	-	-	-	1.0	1.2	1.1	6.4	8.2	7.4	-	-	7.1	14.9	18.8	16.8	13.2	14.8	13.8	-	-	-	-	-	-

Author	Scientific name	Type	n	Fe (mg/kg)			Zn (mg/kg)			Se (mg/kg)			I (mg/kg)			Mg (g/kg)			K (g/kg)			Cu (mg/kg)			Mn (mg/kg)			B (mg/kg)			Mo (mg/kg)			Ni (mg/kg)		
				min	max	mean	min	max	mean	min	max	mean	min	max	mean	min	max	mean	min	max	mean	min	max	mean	min	max	mean	min	max	mean	min	max	mean	min	max	mean
[63]	*Glycine max* (L.) Merr.	C	-	-	-	164.0	-	-	27.0	-	-	-	-	-	-	-	-	2.6	-	-	-	-	-	-	-	-	-	-	-	-	-	-	-	-	-	-
[64]		G	-	-	-	-	-	-	-	-	-	-	-	-	1.8	-	-	-	-	-	-	-	-	-	-	-	-	-	-	-	-	-	-	-	-	-
[65]		G	3	38.6	115.1	54.9	-	-	-	-	-	-	-	-	-	0.1	0.1	0.1	-	-	-	-	-	-	-	-	-	-	-	-	-	-	-	-	-	-
[66]		G	-	-	-	-	-	-	-	-	-	-	-	-	-	1.6	3.4	0.0	9.3	23.9	17.2	-	-	-	-	-	-	-	-	-	-	-	-	-	-	-
[67]		G	27	48.0	81.0	65.0	-	-	-	-	-	-	-	-	-	-	-	-	-	-	-	-	-	-	27.0	36.0	33.0	-	-	-	-	-	-	-	-	-
[44]	*Pisum sativum* L.	L	152	38.6	320.9	67.9	11.3	82.9	41.7	-	-	-	-	-	-	-	-	-	6.7	18.7	13.1	10.5	50.8	18.3	10.2	37.9	15.8	-	-	-	-	-	-	-	-	-
[68]		L	3	6.9	22.9	11.4	7.0	18.3	31.1	-	-	-	-	-	-	0.0	0.1	0.0	0.0	0.1	0.1	0.9	1.9	1.2	1.3	2.1	1.6	-	-	-	-	-	-	-	-	-
[44]		C	5	61.6	87.7	73.3	25.7	43.6	34.2	-	-	-	-	-	-	-	-	-	11.9	18.4	14.5	19.8	26.3	21.7	16.2	20.9	19.0	-	-	-	-	-	-	-	-	-
[34]		C	-	-	-	-	-	-	-	-	-	-	0.1	0.2	0.1	-	-	-	-	-	-	-	-	-	-	-	-	-	-	-	-	-	-	-	-	-
[69]		C	7	39.2	42.3	41.0	25.8	30.6	29.6	-	-	-	-	-	-	1.2	1.4	1.3	8.0	8.9	8.3	5.9	6.8	6.2	7.9	9.5	8.6	8.1	10.1	9.3	-	-	-	-	-	-
[48]	*Cajanus cajan* (L.) Millsp.	L	14	33.0	66.0	45.3	20.5	38.6	28.0	-	-	-	-	-	-	1.2	1.8	1.4	8.9	15.8	13.0	8.7	14.3	11.2	9.0	73.1	23.3	-	-	-	-	-	-	-	-	-
[64]	*Vigna unguiculata* (L.) Walp.	G	-	-	-	-	-	-	-	-	-	-	-	-	1.0	-	-	-	-	-	-	-	-	-	-	-	-	-	-	-	-	-	-	-	-	-
[45]	*Vigna subterranea* (L.) Walp.	L	12	5.8	292.0	153.4	30.3	56.0	33.9	-	-	-	-	-	-	4.2	5.2	4.7	3.1	4.4	3.7	3.7	9.1	6.3	-	-	-	-	-	-	-	-	-	-	-	-
		L	1	-	-	92.4	-	-	45.6	-	-	-	-	-	-	-	-	5.2	-	-	4.0	-	-	6.3	-	-	-	-	-	-	-	-	-	-	-	-
		L	1	-	-	212.7	-	-	60.4	-	-	-	-	-	-	-	-	4.3	-	-	4.1	-	-	7.1	-	-	-	-	-	-	-	-	-	-	-	-
		L	5	73.6	246.5	164.1	30.2	49.9	34.2	-	-	-	-	-	-	4.0	5.5	4.9	3.1	4.1	3.6	6.8	45.7	16.7	-	-	-	-	-	-	-	-	-	-	-	-
		L	9	113.7	555.1	250.2	26.0	61.3	34.5	-	-	-	-	-	-	4.2	4.8	4.6	3.3	4.0	3.6	3.3	21.5	9.6	-	-	-	-	-	-	-	-	-	-	-	-
		L	2	66.5	122.2	94.4	31.9	39.2	42.5	-	-	-	-	-	-	4.3	5.2	4.8	3.5	4.3	3.9	5.9	7.1	6.5	-	-	-	-	-	-	-	-	-	-	-	-
		L	3	89.0	253.0	165.6	32.3	39.1	26.3	-	-	-	-	-	-	4.4	4.8	4.6	3.1	3.7	3.4	4.8	6.1	5.4	-	-	-	-	-	-	-	-	-	-	-	-
		L	7	132.2	364.2	229.3	35.2	58.0	36.8	-	-	-	-	-	-	4.6	5.6	5.0	3.4	4.1	3.7	3.9	8.0	5.9	-	-	-	-	-	-	-	-	-	-	-	-
[64]	*Arachis hypogaea* L.	G	-	-	-	-	-	-	-	-	-	-	-	-	0.9	-	-	-	-	-	-	-	-	-	-	-	-	-	-	-	-	-	-	-	-	-

Table 1.
Mineral concentration ranges (minimum, maximum, and mean) reported in international studies for major pulse species: lentils (lens culinaris medik.), faba beans (vicia faba L.), chickpeas (cicer arietinum L.), common beans (phaseolus vulgaris L.), peas (pisum sativum L.), Bambara groundnuts (vigna subterranea (L.) Verdc.), pigeonpeas (cajanus cajan (L.) Millsp.), soybeans (glycine max (L.) Merr.), and cowpea (vigna unguiculata (L.) Walp.). Seed types include landraces (L), commercial varieties (C), and germplasm accessions (G). The column "n" indicates the number of genotypes evaluated in each study. Mineral concentrations are expressed as mg kg^{-1} (Fe, Zn, Se, I, Cu, Mn, B, Mo, Ni) or g kg^{-1} (Mg, K). A dash (-) indicates that the data was not reported or not detected in the original study [49–69].

Turkey, Morocco, Spain, Ethiopia, Chile, Brazil, Portugal, the Mesoamerican and Andean centers, and several sub-Saharan African nations. It focuses on nutrients critical for alleviating hidden hunger: Fe, Zn, Mg, K, Cu, Mn, B, Mo, and Ni. Data on selenium and iodine remain scarce despite their nutritional importance; the few available studies consistently report low baseline iodine concentrations, underscoring the need for biofortification [32–34]. The table also includes germplasm accessions from global gene banks, which predominantly preserve traditional landraces and wild relatives – valued as reservoirs of functional alleles – while also incorporating modern cultivars and advanced breeding lines [35, 36]; thus, they represent a valuable source of diversity.

Multiple studies have reported significant differences in mineral concentration between landraces and commercial varieties across various legume species. The majority of these studies demonstrate the nutritional superiority of landraces. For instance, Benbrahim [37] found that Moroccan lentil landraces significantly outperformed commercial varieties in Fe, Mg, Ca, P, and Mn. Similarly, Baloch [38] reported that Turkish *V. faba* landraces showed significantly higher mineral concentrations than commercial cultivars, with maximum Zn values doubling those of modern varieties. [15] observed that common bean landraces surpassed commercial lines in Se (by 2–3 fold) and Zn. Gorbe *et al.* [39] documented superior Mg, Cu, Mn, Ni, or Mo retention in Spanish *V. faba* landraces compared to the commercial 'Mutxamel'. In common beans, Gorbe *et al.* [40] reported that cluster analysis placed the commercial variety 'Big Borlotto' in a low-mineral group, while landraces from other clusters exhibited significantly higher mineral levels. Karaköy *et al.* [41] confirmed similar trends in lentils. However, exceptions exist where commercial varieties exhibited higher mineral content, sometimes resulting from targeted biofortification breeding. Bevilaqua and Antunes [42] found that modern black bean lines in Brazil contained significantly higher Fe and Mn than traditional varieties. Grewal et al. [43] reported that recently released commercial *C. arietinum* cultivars in India outperformed landraces in Zn and Fe. Notably, Demirbas [44] presented a mixed scenario: while landraces excelled in P and Zn, commercial *P. sativum* showed superior K, Fe, Cu, and Mn. Overall, the evidence consistently favors landraces for having higher nutrient concentration, whereas commercial varieties usually surpass them when specific breeding programs have prioritised biofortification.

The mineral diversity in legumes exhibits variability ranges that far exceed levels found in modern varieties, establishing a high 'nutritional ceiling' for biofortification. Analyzing maximum recorded values rather than group means is critical for identifying the biological potential of these crops, as averages often mask exceptional genotypes possessing unique allelic variation for mineral translocation. Across the studies reviewed (**Table 1**), almost all of the highest mineral concentrations were found in landraces across multiple legume species. In bambara groundnut, Alake and Alake [45] reported exceptionally high iron levels reaching 555.1 mg kg^{-1} and magnesium concentrations of 5.6 g kg^{-1}. For common bean, Murube et al. [46] documented zinc values up to 96.5 mg kg^{-1}, selenium reaching 6 mg kg^{-1}, and nickel levels of 9.8 mg kg^{-1}. In faba bean, Karaköy et al. [47] found potassium concentrations as high as 56 g kg^{-1}. Pea showed copper levels of 50.8 mg kg^{-1} [44], while pigeonpea exhibited manganese concentrations of 73.1 mg kg^{-1} [48]. Only for boron did a commercial common bean variety show a higher concentration (29 mg kg^{-1}) than the landraces evaluated [49]. Regarding iodine (I), available data are too scarce to draw meaningful comparisons between landraces and commercial varieties. These findings consistently demonstrate the superior mineral density of landraces compared to commercial varieties across most essential micronutrients. The widest ranges between maximum and minimum mineral concentrations within a single study were reported by Alake and Alake [45] in bambara groundnut (*V. subterranea*), with iron (Fe) values spanning from 113.7 to 555.1 mg kg^{-1}. Similarly, Murube *et al.* [46] documented a broad zinc (Zn) range in common bean (*P. vulgaris*), from 2.4 to 96.5 mg kg^{-1}. In pigeonpea (*C. cajan*), Mashifane et al. [48] observed manganese (Mn) concentrations varying between 9.0 and 73.1 mg kg^{-1}. These wide intra-specific ranges highlight the substantial genetic diversity preserved within landraces and their potential as donors for biofortification breeding.

4. Comprehensive strategies for harnessing landrace potential

The nutritional superiority of legume landraces translates into a wide spectrum of practical applications. This section explores their multifunctional potential across five key domains: (1) as donor parents in biofortification breeding programs; (2) as high-value products in emerging niche markets for health-conscious consumers; (3) as functional ingredients in the food and pharmaceutical industries; (4) as mineral-dense components in animal nutrition; and (5) as strategic tools for agroecological restoration, including green manuring and soil microbiota regeneration.

4.1 Natural biofortification

Landraces offer a 'low-cost and eco-friendly approach' to genetic biofortification [70], often possessing superior 'transporter genetics' – alleles that govern mineral translocation from roots to seeds – which are frequently silenced in commercial varieties [71]. This potential has been successfully realised across multiple crops. A 2023 study on sorghum, using Indian landraces, developed 19 improved genotypes with significant gains: crude protein increased by up to 32.25%, total phenolics by 18.48%, and antioxidant activity by 15.43%, achieving iron levels of 14.21–28.41 mg/100 g and zinc levels of 4.81–8.16 mg/100 g [70].

Landraces with high mineral content are routinely used in breeding programs for wheat, rice, and lentils through conventional crossing and backcrossing [72–74]. Garg *et al.* [75], documented successful biofortification efforts in legumes include the development of iron-enriched bean varieties through the international HarvestPlus program, which targets beans as one of its key biofortified staple crops alongside wheat, rice, maize, cassava, pearl millet, and sweet potato. In common bean (*Phaseolus vulgaris* L.), these efforts have proven particularly promising: studies indicate that iron content could be increased by 60%–80% and zinc by 50%. This success is underpinned by the high heritability observed for both iron and zinc content in common bean, making it a highly responsive crop for biofortification breeding.

4.2 A new market for health-conscious consumers

Beyond their role in breeding programs, legume landraces hold significant commercial potential in emerging niche markets for health-conscious consumers. These markets specifically target cultivars with exceptional micronutrient density and low levels of antinutritional factors (ANFs) – secondary metabolites that reduce nutrient bioavailability — such as protease inhibitors, tannins, phytates, oxalates, and flatus-producing oligosaccharides [76–78].

Indeed, consumer interest in nutrient-dense foods is growing substantially: recent surveys show that 18% of consumers actively seek more nutrient-dense options – a 50% increase since 2021 – with Spain reaching 23% and Brazil 37% [79]. Choice experiments confirm that consumers are willing to pay premium prices for traditional varieties, accepting an additional €0.90/kg for ancient tomato landraces [80]. Multiple reviews document a broader shift toward health-conscious consumption, with increased consideration of the health and nutritional aspects of food [81] and an increasing trend among consumers focusing on traditional landraces [82].

In the Spanish market, 2024 consumption data reveal a strategic opportunity for nutrient-dense legume landraces: despite a general contraction in food demand, household legume purchases grew by 2.8% in volume [83]. This growth is driven by a shift toward convenience, with ready-to-eat cooked legumes now accounting for 57.5% of household volume. To effectively combat hidden hunger, landraces' superior nutritional profiles must be delivered through these formats, which appeal to younger households seeking healthy, Mediterranean-style meals. Commercial viability is further reinforced by a 13.5% surge in out-of-home legume consumption, as traditional dishes regain relevance in restaurants [83]. This renewed interest in culinary heritage offers a powerful platform to position landraces as premium ingredients that provide both cultural value and essential micronutrients often lacking in modern diets.

This market opportunity is already being translated into concrete action through several international initiatives. The Erasmus + project 'Niche Market Farming', for instance, is actively training farmers and food professionals across Europe to bring ancient varieties to consumers through local food networks and quality product markets [84]. Simultaneously, frameworks developed by Bioversity International and IFAD are being implemented in Asia, Africa, and Latin America to reintroduce neglected and underutilised species into local diets, with documented success in mainstreaming nutrient-dense crops like millets in rural India [85]. These initiatives demonstrate that, alongside commercial varieties, a parallel market for nutrient-dense landraces – targeting health-conscious consumers and food-insecure communities alike – is not merely a theoretical possibility but an emerging reality.

4.3 The emerging functional food and pharmaceutical market

In the context of functional foods, landraces are not just raw materials but high-value ingredients. Their unique phytochemical profiles, including high concentrations of anthocyanins and phenolic compounds, fibre, and resistant starch, act synergistically with their mineral content. For instance, some studies have reported high levels of antioxidants in pigmented landraces of *P. vulgaris* (black and purple beans) [86] and high resistant starch content in specific chickpea cultivars [87]. Legume flours represent nutrient-rich ingredients for healthy processed foods, a market trend supported by the successful launch of gluten-free pasta and snacks incorporating flour from high-protein lentil and chickpea landraces in North American and European markets.

These applications are already a commercial reality [88]. Legume flours are actively incorporated at 2%–30% levels in bakery products, pasta, meat alternatives, and gluten-free formulations, improving fiber, protein, and phenolic profiles without compromising consumer acceptance [89, 90]. Pulse protein isolates and concentrates are increasingly used as meat extenders, milk substitutes, and in gluten-free products [88], while legume flours' functional properties – solubility and water-binding capacity – make them particularly suitable for gluten-free bakery and pasta applications [91].

Furthermore, the pharmaceutical and nutraceutical industries could utilise selected landraces as high-purity sources for extracting plant-based proteins, bioactive compounds, and chelated minerals, catering to the growing demand for vegan and clean-label supplements. Emerging research supports this potential: legume-derived ingredients can function as pharmaceutical excipients [92], while specific compounds like kievitone show anticancer properties, and agmatine and isovitexin exhibit antimicrobial activity [93]. Bioactive peptides from legumes can induce cancer cell death [94], and legume polyphenols demonstrate antioxidant, anti-inflammatory, and anti-diabetic effects [95]. However, most evidence remains preclinical, with significant challenges in cost, safety, and availability before widespread pharmaceutical use becomes viable [96].

4.4 The trophic pathway: Landraces in animal nutrition

Legumes are a cornerstone of livestock diets, fulfilling a dual role clearly distinguished in the literature: grain legumes (e.g., peas, faba beans) are primarily utilised in monogastric nutrition (poultry and swine) due to their high protein content, averaging 25–45 g per 100 g of dry matter, while fodder legumes (e.g., alfalfa, clover) are mainly used in ruminant nutrition as high-quality forage [97]. For ruminants, the high protein content of forage legumes represents a key nutritional advantage [98]; they are well-validated for sustainable ruminant production [99], and beyond macronutrients, they serve as a natural delivery system for micronutrients [100].

In addition, while conventional livestock systems rely on synthetic mineral supplements to prevent deficiencies, these inorganic salts often suffer from poor bioavailability [101], with minerals typically added at 20–30 times the normal requirement, resulting in excess excretion and subsequent environmental pollution [102, 103]. Thus, conventional supplementation creates both nutritional inefficiency and environmental runoff from manure contamination [104]. In this context, the integration of mineral-dense legume landraces into animal feed offers a significant advantage over these chemical additives. However, while legume landraces contain high mineral concentrations, their bioavailability is limited by phytic acid, which forms insoluble complexes with minerals [105, 106]. Therefore, realising this advantage requires selecting landraces with lower phytate content or applying processing techniques – such as fermentation and germination – that can reduce phytates by up to 26%–85% and significantly improve mineral bioavailability [107, 108].

Economically, while synthetic supplements may appear cheaper in the short term, mineral-rich landraces offer greater long-term profitability by reducing veterinary costs through improved animal resilience [109]. Moreover, this improved animal health translates directly into higher-quality products, as efficient mineral uptake naturally enriches meat, milk, and eggs for human consumption [110]. In addition, these 'super-nutritive' landraces are particularly vital for organic farming, where synthetic vitamins and inorganic mineral boluses are strictly restricted or prohibited [111].

4.5 Agroecological restoration

As previously stated, restoring nutrient-depleted soils requires integrated practices that increase organic matter and enhance soil biodiversity. Key strategies include crop rotations, cover crops, organic amendments, residue retention, and reduced tillage [112, 113]. The use of cover crops – particularly in woody cropping systems, where they are sown in interrows – has gained significant policy support under the current CAP 2023–2027, being explicitly recognised within eco-schemes as a practice that protects soil, enhances biodiversity, and contributes to carbon farming objectives [114]. Recent research emphasises that plant residues and field biomass are particularly promising for nutrient replenishment, while biochar serves as a key component for enriching soil organic carbon [115]. The central goal is to rebuild soil organic carbon above critical thresholds [116] to restore soil structure, water retention, and fertility, while harnessing the interdependence of soil properties with biodiversity at the core [117]. This approach aligns with novel solutions that integrate biological, physical, and chemical strategies carefully adapted to specific site conditions [118].

Legumes play a multifunctional role within this framework. As nitrogen-fixing plants, they enrich soils while providing high-quality biomass. Legume-based complex rotations are applicable under most agricultural conditions [112], while their residues serve as green manure – a recognised nature-based solution for maintaining soil fertility [119]. This green manuring process releases nutrients slowly. Thus, reintroducing legumes, particularly nutrient-dense landraces adapted to low-input conditions, is a cornerstone of sustainable soil restoration.

In addition, legume landraces often possess a sophisticated genetic architecture for recruiting beneficial soil microbiota, a trait that has been significantly eroded in modern cultivars through the 'domestication syndrome'. Unlike high-yielding commercial varieties selected under nutrient-saturated conditions, landraces evolved in resource-limited environments, necessitating the conservation of complex chemical signalling pathways to attract symbiotic partners [120]. Research indicates that these traditional genotypes exhibit a more diverse repertoire of root exudates, including specific flavonoids and strigolactones, which serve as critical chemotactic signals for *Rhizobium* and AMF [121]. Furthermore, the reliance on synthetic inputs in modern breeding has led to a 'disruption of symbiosis', where plants have lost the metabolic incentive to invest carbon in microbial exchange, whereas landraces maintain robust stress-induced signalling pathways involved in microbial recruitment [122].

On the other hand, the adoption of conservation agriculture, which sustains healthy microbial communities, is imperative. Implementing no-tillage (or reduced tillage) together with the application of sustainable fertilizers and the use of cover crops or crop rotation would preserve the integrity of microorganisms and fungal mycelia. Furthermore, the application of microbial inoculants, such as specific *Rhizobium* strains, would actively catalyse the solubilisation of zinc and iron, effectively biofortifying the legume crops through natural symbiotic pathways [123].

5. Conclusion and future perspectives

The evidence presented in this chapter demonstrates that the challenge of low nutrient density in modern legumes is not solely a problem of soil exhaustion, but rather the result of a complex interplay between genetic, agronomic, and microbiological factors. The Green Revolution's singular focus on yield maximisation has inadvertently selected for cultivars with reduced mineral content and a weakened capacity to engage in beneficial symbioses with soil microorganisms. This 'dilution effect', compounded by intensive agricultural practices that degrade soil microbial communities, has systematically undermined the nutritional quality of these crops.

In this context, legume landraces emerge not as relics of the past but as essential resources for the future of sustainable and nutritious food systems. Their documented nutritional superiority represents a genetic treasure trove that remains largely untapped. This superiority stems from a dual advantage: first, from alleles that govern efficient mineral translocation to seeds, which have been silenced in commercial varieties; and second, from a sophisticated genetic architecture for recruiting beneficial microbiota, a trait eroded through the 'domestication syndrome'.

The practical applications of this potential are already being realised across multiple fronts. In breeding programs, landraces have proven their value as donor parents for biofortification, with documented successes in crops such as common beans and lentils. In the marketplace, growing consumer demand for nutrient-dense foods is creating viable niches for traditional varieties, supported by demonstrated willingness to pay premium prices and by European initiatives actively training farmers to bring these products to consumers. The functional food sector is increasingly incorporating legume flours into bakery, pasta, and meat-alternative products, capitalising on their techno-functional properties and nutritional profiles. In livestock systems, mineral-dense landraces with low ANF content offer an alternative to the environmental and economic costs of inorganic supplementation. Finally, in the realm of agroecological restoration, legumes – and particularly landraces adapted to low-input conditions – play a multifunctional role as nitrogen fixers, green manures, and facilitators of soil microbial regeneration. However, realising this potential requires a paradigm shift. Conservation alone is insufficient; landraces must be actively integrated into breeding programs, value chains, and agricultural systems. This integration must also be supported by policies that recognise the value of genetic diversity and create market incentives for nutrient-dense products.

In conclusion, addressing hidden hunger through legumes requires moving beyond the false dichotomy of 'yield versus nutrition'. The way forward lies in a dual strategy that combines the genetic potential of landraces with the ecological wisdom of agroecological practices. By restoring both the genes that govern mineral density and the microbial partnerships that enable their expression, we can begin to rebuild food systems that are not only productive but also truly nourishing.

Acknowledgements

This work was funded by the Grupos Emergentes GVA Project (Bajoqueta Resilience-CIGE/2024/237) and the IVIA-GVA 52401B project of the Valencian

Institute of Agricultural Research (co-funded by the European Union through the ERDF 2021–2027 Programme of the Valencian Community). Irene Moreno was supported by a predoctoral contract funded by the "Marisa Badenes" program of the Generalitat Valenciana, which may be co-financed by the European Union through the European Social Fund Plus (ESF+) Comunitat Valenciana 2021–2027 program.

The authors acknowledge the use of DeepSeek (an AI tool) for language polishing and the use of Elicit (an AI tool) for literature search in the preparation of this manuscript.

Author details

Elisa Gorbe[†], Irene Moreno-Valle[†] and Consuelo Penella*

Valencian Institute of Agricultural Research (IVIA), Moncada, Spain

† These authors are equally contributed

*Address all correspondence to: penella_con@gva.es

References

[1] United Nations. The Sustainable Development Goals Report 2020. 2020. Available from: https://unstats.un.org/sdgs/report/2020/The-Sustainable-Development-Goals-Report-2020.pdf

[2] Gödecke T, Stein AJ, Qaim M. The global burden of chronic and hidden hunger: Trends and determinants. Global Food Security. 2018;**17**:21–29. DOI: 10.1016/j.gfs.2018.03.004

[3] Lowe NM. The global challenge of hidden hunger: Perspectives from the field. Proceedings of the Nutrition Society. 2021;**80**(3):283–289. DOI: 10.1017/S0029665121000902

[4] Stevens GA, Beal T, Mbuya MNN, Luo H, Neufeld LM. Micronutrient deficiencies among preschool-aged children and women of reproductive age worldwide: A pooled analysis of individual-level data from population-representative surveys. The Lancet Global Health. 2022;**10**(11):e1590–e1599. DOI: 10.1016/S2214-109X(22)00367-9

[5] FAO, IFAD, UNICEF, WFP, & WHO. The State of Food Security and Nutrition in the World 2025-Addressing High Food Price Inflation for Food Security and Nutrition. Rome, Italy: FAO; IFAD; UNICEF; WFP; WHO; 2025. DOI: 10.4060/cd6008en

[6] Popkin BM, Corvalan C, Grummer-Strawn LM. Dynamics of the double burden of malnutrition and the changing nutrition reality. The Lancet. 2020;**395**(10217):65–74. DOI: 10.1016/S0140-6736(19)32497-3

[7] Martín-Cabrejas MÁ. Legumes: Nutritional quality, processing and potential health benefits. 2019

[8] FAO. FAOSTAT Statistical Database. Food and Agriculture Organization of the United Nations. 2024. Available from: https://www.fao.org/faostat/en/ [Accessed: 2026-February-12]

[9] Peoples MB, Ladha JK, Herridge DF. Enhancing legume N2 fixation through plant and soil management. Plant and Soil. 1995;**174**(1–2):83–101. DOI: 10.1007/BF00032242

[10] Mazzoncini M, Sapkota TB, Bàrberi P, Antichi D, Risaliti R. Long-term effect of tillage, nitrogen fertilization and cover crops on soil organic carbon and total nitrogen content. Soil and Tillage Research. 2011;**114**(2):165–174. DOI: 10.1016/j.still.2011.05.001

[11] Council of the European Union. Council conclusions on carbon farming. 2022. Available from: https://www.consilium.europa.eu/es/press/press-releases/2022/04/07/council-adopts-conclusions-on-carbon-farming/pdf/ [Accessed: 2026-February-12]

[12] OECD/FAO. OECD-FAO Agricultural Outlook 2025-2034. Paris/FAO, Rome: OECD Publishing; 2025. DOI: 10.1787/601276cd-en

[13] Davis DR. Declining Fruit and Vegetable Nutrient Composition: What Is the Evidence? HortScience. 2009;**44**(1):15–19. DOI: 10.21273/HORTSCI.44.1.15

[14] Fan M-S, Zhao F-J, Fairweather-Tait SJ, Poulton PR, Dunham SJ, McGrath SP. Evidence of decreasing mineral density in wheat grain over the last 160 years. Journal of Trace Elements in Medicine and Biology.

2008;**22**(4):315–324. DOI: 10.1016/j.jtemb.2008.07.002

[15] Celmeli T, Sari H, Canci H, Sari D, Adak A, Eker T, Toker C. The Nutritional Content of Common Bean (Phaseolus vulgaris L.) Landraces in Comparison to Modern Varieties. Agronomy. 2018;**8**(9):166. DOI: 10.3390/agronomy8090166

[16] Hammer K, Knüpffer H, Xhuveli L, Perrino P. Estimating genetic erosion in landraces? two case studies. Genetic Resources and Crop Evolution. 1996;**43**(4):329–336. DOI: 10.1007/BF00132952

[17] Lajusticia Bergasa AM. El Magnesio. Spain: Plaza & Janes; 1979

[18] Pérez-Albela JL. El Magnífico Magnesio. Spain: Diana; 2017

[19] Lyne JW, Barak P. Are Depleted Soils Causing a Reduction in the Mineral Content Of Food Crops? [Poster session]. Annual Meetings of the ASA/CSSA/SSSA; 2000

[20] Marles RJ. Mineral nutrient composition of vegetables, fruits and grains: The context of reports of apparent historical declines. Journal of Food Composition and Analysis. 2017;**56**(4):93–103. DOI: 10.1016/j.jfca.2016.11.012

[21] Mayer A. Historical changes in the mineral content of fruits and vegetables. British Food Journal. 1997;**99**(6):207–211. DOI: 10.1108/00070709710181540

[22] Rengel Z. Availability of Mn, Zn and Fe in the rhizosphere. Journal of Soil Science and Plant Nutrition. 2015;**15**(2). DOI: 10.4067/S0718-95162015005000036

[23] Saha M, Sarkar S, Sarkar B, Sharma BK, Bhattacharjee S, Tribedi P. Microbial siderophores and their potential applications: A review. Environmental Science and Pollution Research. 2016;**23**(5):3984–3999. DOI: 10.1007/s11356-015-4294-0

[24] Jacoby R, Peukert M, Succurro A, Koprivova A, Kopriva S. The Role of Soil Microorganisms in Plant Mineral Nutrition—Current Knowledge and Future Directions. Frontiers in Plant Science. 2017;8. DOI: 10.3389/fpls.2017.01617

[25] Trivedi P, Delgado-Baquerizo M, Anderson IC, Singh BK. Response of soil properties and microbial communities to agriculture: Implications for primary productivity and soil health indicators. Frontiers in Plant Science. 2016;**7**:7. DOI: 10.3389/fpls.2016.00990

[26] Treseder KK. Nitrogen additions and microbial biomass: A meta-analysis of ecosystem studies. Ecology Letters. 2008;**11**(10):1111–1120. DOI: 10.1111/j.1461-0248.2008.01230.x

[27] Verbruggen E, Toby Kiers E. Evolutionary ecology of mycorrhizal functional diversity in agricultural systems. Evolutionary Applications. 2010;**3**(5–6):547–560. DOI: 10.1111/j.1752-4571.2010.00145.x

[28] Lo CC. Effect of pesticides on soil microbial community. Journal of Environmental Science and Health, Part B. 2010;**45**(5):348–359. DOI: 10.1080/03601231003799804

[29] Zabaloy MC, Garland JL, Gómez MA. An integrated approach to evaluate the impacts of the herbicides glyphosate, 2,4-D and metsulfuron-methyl on soil microbial communities in the Pampas region, Argentina. Applied Soil Ecology. 2008;**40**(1):1–12. DOI: 10.1016/j.apsoil.2008.02.004

[30] Janzen HH. The soil carbon dilemma: Shall we hoard it or use it? Soil Biology and Biochemistry. 2006;**38** (3):419–424. DOI: 10.1016/j.soilbio.2005.10.008

[31] Helgason T, Daniell TJ, Husband R, Fitter AH, Young JPW. Ploughing up the wood-wide web? Nature. 1998;**394**(6692):431–431. DOI: 10.1038/28764

[32] Dobosy P, Kröpfl K, Óvári M, Sandil S, Németh K, Engloner A, Takács T, Záray G. Biofortification of green bean (Phaseolus vulgaris L.) and lettuce (Lactuca sativa L.) with iodine in a plant-calcareous sandy soil system irrigated with water containing KI. Journal of Food Composition and Analysis. 2020;**88**:103434. DOI: 10.1016/j.jfca.2020.103434

[33] Paśko P, Prochownik E, Kryczyk-Kozioł J, Jlassi M, Yahyaoui D, Galanty A, Ben Ahmed H, Dobrowolska-Iwanek J. Iodine fortification of edible legume sprouts: A pilot biofortification study. Foods. 2025;**14**(21):3691. DOI: 10.3390/foods14213691

[34] Vetési V, Záray G, Endrédi A, Sandil S, Rékási M, Takács T, Dobosy P. Iodine biofortification of bean (Phaseolus vulgaris L.) and pea (Pisum sativum L.) plants cultivated in three different soils. PLOS ONE. 2022;**17**(10): e0275589. DOI: 10.1371/journal.pone.0275589

[35] Bhullar NK, Street K, Mackay M, Yahiaoui N, Keller B. Unlocking wheat genetic resources for the molecular identification of previously undescribed functional alleles at the Pm3 resistance locus. Proceedings of the National Academy of Sciences. 2009;**106** (23):9519–9524. DOI: 10.1073/pnas.0904152106

[36] Parzies HK, Spoor W, Ennos RA. Genetic diversity of barley landrace accessions (Hordeum vulgare ssp. vulgare) conserved for different lengths of time in ex situ gene banks. Heredity. 2000;**84**(4):476–486. DOI: 10.1046/j.1365-2540.2000.00705.x

[37] Benbrahim N, Gaboun F, Mentag R, Taghouti M. The genetic potential of Moroccan lentil landraces. International Journal of Agricultural. 2019;**9**(3):291–306

[38] Baloch FS, Karaköy T, Demirbas A, Toklu F, Özkan H, Hatipoglu R. Variation of some seed mineral contents in open pollinated faba bean (Vicia faba L.) landraces from Turkey. Turkish Journal of Agriculture and Forestry. 2014;**38**:591–602. DOI: 10.3906/tar-1311-31

[39] Gorbe E, Moreno-Valle I, Calatayud Á, Penella C. Unraveling diversity in physical and mineral traits of faba bean (Vicia faba L.) landraces harvested at immature stages. Horticulturae. 2025b;**11**(12):1411. DOI: 10.3390/horticulturae11121411

[40] Gorbe E, Morard M, Rausell-Moreno A, Calatayud Á, Penella C. Exploring nutritional quality and bioactive compounds in Mediterranean bean landraces. Journal of Food Composition and Analysis. 2025a;**142**:107433. DOI: 10.1016/j.jfca.2025.107433

[41] Karaköy T, Erdem H, Baloch FS, Toklu F, Eker S, Kilian B, Özkan H. Diversity of Macro- and Micronutrients in the Seeds of Lentil Landraces. The Scientific World Journal. 2012;**2012**:1–9. DOI: 10.1100/2012/710412

[42] Bevilaqua GAP, Antunes IF. Chemical composition of whole grains in common beans landraces and

breeding genotypes. HOLOS. 2015;**2**:81–91. DOI: 10.15628/holos.2015.1996

[43] Grewal SK, Sharma KP, Bharadwaj RD, Hegde V, Tripathi S, Singh S, Kumar Jain P, Kumar Agrawal P, Mondal B. Understanding genotypic variation and identification of promising genotypes for iron and zinc content in chickpea (Cicer arietinum L.). Journal of Food Composition and Analysis. 2020;**88**:103458. DOI: 10.1016/j.jfca.2020.103458

[44] Demirbas A. Micro and Macronutrients Diversity in Turkish Pea (Pisum sativum) Germplasm. International Journal of Agriculture & Biology. 2018a;**20**:701–710. DOI: 10.17957/ijab/15.0545

[45] Alake CO, Alake OO. Genetic diversity for agro-nutritional traits in african landraces of Vigna subterranean Germplasm. Journal of Crop Improvement. 2016;**30**(4):378–398. DOI: 10.1080/15427528.2016.1171817

[46] Murube E, Beleggia R, Pacetti D, Nartea A, Frascarelli G, Lanzavecchia G, Bellucci E, Nanni L, Gioia T, Marciello U, Esposito S, Foresi G, Logozzo G, Frega GN, Bitocchi E, Papa R. Characterization of nutritional quality traits of a common bean germplasm collection. Foods. 2021;**10**(7):1572. DOI: 10.3390/foods10071572

[47] Karaköy T, Demirbaş A, Toklu F, Gürsoy N, Tugay Karagöl E, Uncuer D, Özkan H. Assessment of micro and macro nutrients contents in the Turkish faba bean germplasm. "Agriculture for Life, Life for Agriculture" Conference Proceedings. 2018;**1**(1):72–78. DOI: 10.2478/alife-2018-0011

[48] Mashifane DC, Chiulele RM, Gwata ET. Diversity in Selected Grain Mineral and Protein among Pigeonpea Landraces. Applied Sciences. 2024;**14**(2):573. DOI: 10.3390/app14020573

[49] Márquez K, Arriagada O, Pérez-Díaz R, Cabeza RA, Plaza A, Arévalo B, Meisel LA, Ojeda D, Silva H, Schwember AR, Fuentes C, Flores M, Carrasco B. Nutritional Characterization of Chilean Landraces of Common Bean. Plants. 2024;**13**(6):817. DOI: 10.3390/plants13060817

[50] Moraghan JT, Grafton K. Genetic diversity and mineral composition of common bean seed. Journal of the Science of Food and Agriculture. 2001;**81**(4):404–408. DOI: 10.1002/1097-0010(200103)81:4<404::AID-JSFA822>3.0.CO;2-H

[51] Blair MW, Astudillo C, Grusak MA, Graham R, Beebe SE. Inheritance of seed iron and zinc concentrations in common bean (Phaseolus vulgaris L.). Molecular Breeding. 2009;**23**(2):197–207. DOI: 10.1007/s11032-008-9225-z

[52] Chávez-Mendoza C, Sánchez E. Bioactive compounds from mexican varieties of the Common Bean (Phaseolus vulgaris): Implications for health. Molecules. 2017;**22**(8):1360. DOI: 10.3390/molecules22081360

[53] Islam FMA, Basford KE, Jara C, Redden RJ, Beebe S. Seed compositional and disease resistance differences among gene pools in cultivated common bean. Genetic Resources and Crop Evolution. 2002;**49**(3):285–293. DOI: 10.1023/A:1015510428026

[54] Pinheiro C, Baeta JP, Pereira AM, Domingues H, Ricardo CP. Diversity of seed mineral composition of Phaseolus vulgaris L. germplasm. Journal of Food Composition and Analysis. 2010;**23**

(4):319–325. DOI: 10.1016/j.jfca.2010.01.005

[55] Toklu F, Biçer BT, Karaköy T.Agro-morphological characterization of the Turkish lentil landraces. African Journal of Biotechnology. 2009;**8**(17):4121–4127

[56] Vargas A, Podder R, Subedi M, Bett KE, Vandenberg A. Variability in mineral composition of Canadian lentil genotypes. Canadian Journal of Plant Science. 2025;**105**:1–11. DOI: 10.1139/cjps-2024-0058

[57] Düzgün M, Düz M, Koç M, Erdemci İ. Türkiye'nin Güneydoğusunda Yetişen Bazı Kırmızı Mercimek ve Nohut Çeşitlerinin Mineral Bileşimi. Kahramanmaraş Sütçü Imam Üniversitesi Tarım Ve Doğa Dergisi. 2022;**25**(3):574–580. DOI: 10.18016/ksutarimdoga.vi.941843

[58] Sarker A, Rizvi AH, Singh M. Genetic variability for nutritional quality in Lentil (Lens culinaris Medikus Subsp. culinaris). Legume Research. 2018;**41**(3):363–368. DOI: 10.18805/LR-372

[59] Etemadi F, Barker AV, Hashemi M, Zandvakili OR, Park Y. Nutrient Accumulation in Faba Bean Varieties. Communications in Soil Science and Plant Analysis. 2018;**49**(16):2064–2073. DOI: 10.1080/00103624.2018.1495729

[60] Khazaei H, Vandenberg A. Seed Mineral Composition and Protein Content of Faba Beans (Vicia faba L.) with Contrasting Tannin Contents. Agronomy. 2020;**10**(4):511. DOI: 10.3390/agronomy10040511

[61] Hacisalihoglu G. Analysis of Nutritional Traits: Natural Variation within 90 Diverse Faba Bean (Vicia faba) Genotypes and Daily Value Contribution. Crops. 2024;**4**(3):440–446. DOI: 10.3390/crops4030031

[62] Kose ÖDE, Mut Z. Mineral Contents of Chickpea Cultivars (Cicer arietinum L.) Grown at Different Locations of Turkey. Sains Malaysiana. 2020;**49**(2):293–303. DOI: 10.17576/jsm-2020-4902-07

[63] Etiosa O, Chika N, Benedicta A. Mineral and Proximate Composition of Soya Bean. Asian Journal of Physical and Chemical Sciences. 2018;**4**(3):1–6. DOI: 10.9734/AJOPACS/2017/38530

[64] Salau BA, Ketiku AO, Ajani E, Enzima EN, Idowu GO, Soladoye MO. Iodine contents of some selected roots/tubers, cereals and legumes consumed in Nigeria. African Journal of Biotechnology. 2008;**7**(23):4328–4330. DOI: 10.5897/AJB08.830

[65] Eshun G.Nutrient composition and functional properties of bean flours of three soya bean varieties from Ghana. African Journal of Food Science and Technology. 2012;**3**(8):176–181

[66] Filippi D, Denardin LGDO, Ambrosini VG, Alves LA, Flores JPM, Martins AP, Pias OHDC, Tiecher T. Concentration and removal of macronutrients by soybean seeds over 45 years in Brazil: A meta-analysis. Revista Brasileira de Ciência Do Solo. 2021;**45**. DOI: 10.36783/18069657rbcs20200186

[67] Moraghan JT, Helms TC. Seed Iron in Diverse Soybean Genotypes. Journal of Plant Nutrition. 2005;**28**(8):1453–1463. DOI: 10.1081/PLN-200067521

[68] Gebreegziabher BG, Tsegay BA. Proximate and mineral composition of Ethiopian pea (Pisum sativum var.

abyssinicum A. Braun) landraces vary across altitudinal ecosystems. Cogent Food & Agriculture. 2020;**6**(1): 1789421. DOI: 10.1080/23311932. 2020.1789421

[69] Franck W, Chen C, Franck S, Mohammed YA, Abdelhamid MT, Miller P, Carr PM, Lamb P, Torrion J, Khan Q, McVay K. Cultivar and environmental impacts on protein and mineral concentrations in peas (Pisum sativum L.). Crop Science. 2024;**64**(1):287–302. DOI: 10.1002/ csc2.21165

[70] Nagesh Kumar MVN, Ramya V, Maheshwaramma S, Ganapathy KN, Govindaraj M, Kavitha K, Vanisree K. Exploiting Indian landraces to develop biofortified grain sorghum with high protein and minerals. Frontiers in Nutrition. 2023;10. DOI: 10.3389/ fnut.2023.1228422

[71] Uauy C, Distelfeld A, Fahima T, Blechl A, Dubcovsky J. A NAC gene regulating senescence improves grain protein, zinc, and iron content in wheat. Science. 2006;**314**(5803):1298–1301. DOI: 10.1126/science.1133649

[72] Jahiruddin M. Biofortification of food crops: A novel strategy for reducing micronutrient malnutrition. Fundamental and Applied Agriculture. 2020;**0**:1. DOI: 10.5455/faa.96078

[73] Meher D, Samantara K, Behera A, Mohapatra SR. Folk rice: Genetic storehouse for biofortification: A review. International Journal of Chemical Studies. 2020;**8**(2):1813–1816. DOI: 10.22271/chemi.2020.v8.i2ab.9025

[74] Sharma V, Choudhary M, Kumar P, Choudhary J, Khokhar J, Kaushik P, Goli S. Harnessing the wild relatives and landraces for Fe and Zn Biofortification in wheat through genetic interventions —A review. Sustainability. 2021; **13** (23):12975. DOI: 10.3390/su132312975

[75] Garg M, Sharma N, Sharma S, Kapoor P, Kumar A, Chunduri V, Arora P. Biofortified crops generated by breeding, agronomy, and transgenic approaches are improving lives of millions of people around the world. Frontiers in Nutrition. 2018;**5**. DOI: 10.3389/fnut.2018.00012

[76] Akande KE, Doma UD, Agu HO, Adamu HM. Major antinutrients found in plant protein sources: Their effect on nutrition. Pakistan Journal of Nutrition. 2010;**9**(8):827–832. DOI: 10.3923/ pjn.2010.827.832

[77] Dangi P, Chaudhary N, Gajwani D, Neha. Antinutritional Factors in Legumes. In: Bangar SP, Siroha A, Kumar M, editors. Handbook of Cereals, Pulses, Roots, and Tubers. 1st ed. London: CRC Press; 2021: 173. DOI: 10. 1201/9781003155508

[78] Ibrahim SS, Habiba RA, Shatta AA, Embaby HE. Effect of soaking, germination, cooking and fermentation on antinutritional factors in cowpeas. Nahrung/Food. 2002;**46**(2):92–95. DOI: 10.1002/1521-3803(20020301)46:2<92:: AID-FOOD92>3.0.CO;2-P

[79] NewNutrition Business. Consumer Briefing 2023: From protein to carbs, mood & mind to nutrient density - our annual 5-country survey of food & health beliefs & behaviour. 2023. Available from: https://www.new-nutri tion.com/nnbReport/display/270 [Accessed: 2026-February-12]

[80] Posadinu CM, Rodriguez M, Madau F, Attene G. The value of agrobiodiversity: An analysis of consumers preference for tomatoes.

Renewable Agriculture and Food Systems. 2022;**37**(3):237–247. DOI: 10.1017/S1742170521000491

[81] Grillo O. Rediscovery of Landraces as a Resource for the Future. London: IntechOpen; 2018. DOI: 10.5772/intechopen.69576

[82] Ashraf AM, Begam SN, Sivagamy K, Vijayashanthi VA, Yogameenakshi P. Exploring the bioactives and therapeutic properties of traditional rice landraces for human health and food security: A review. Asian Journal of Dairy and Food Research, (OF). 2024. DOI: 10.18805/ajdfr.DR-2260

[83] MAPA. Informe anual del consumo alimentario en España 2024. 2024. Available from: https://www.mapa.gob.es/dam/mapa/contenido/alimentacion/temas/consumo-y-tendencias-en-alimentacion/panel-de-consumo-alimentario/ultimos-datos/consumo-2024/informe-consumo-2024-baja.pdf [Accessed: 2026-February-12]

[84] Niche Market Farming. Niche Market Farming [Erasmus + Project]. 2021. Available from: https://nichemarketfarming.eu/ [Accessed: 2026-February-12]

[85] International Fund for Agricultural Development. Making local crops work for nutrition-sensitive agriculture. Rural Voices. https://www.ifad.org/en/w/rural-voices/making-local-crops-work-for-nutrition-sensitive-agriculture [Accessed: 2019-August-27]

[86] Granito M, Paolini M, Pérez S. Polyphenols and antioxidant capacity of Phaseolus vulgaris stored under extreme conditions and processed. LWT - Food Science and Technology. 2008;**41**(6):994–999. DOI: 10.1016/j.lwt.2007.07.014

[87] Sarıkaya S, İnanlar B, Younis HGR, Zhao G, Ye F. Chickpea (Cicer arietinum Linn.) starch: Extraction, composition, structure, properties, modifications and food applications. Grain & Oil Science and Technology. 2025;**8**(2):118–136. DOI: 10.1016/j.gaost.2025.03.003

[88] Affrifah NS, Uebersax MA, Amin S. Nutritional significance, value-added applications, and consumer perceptions of food legumes: A review. Legume Science. 2023;**5**(4). DOI: 10.1002/leg3.192

[89] Alfaro-Diaz A, Escobedo A, Luna-Vital DA, Castillo-Herrera G, Mojica L. Common beans as a source of food ingredients: Techno-functional and biological potential. Comprehensive Reviews in Food Science and Food Safety. 2023;**22**(4):2910–2944. DOI: 10.1111/1541-4337.13166

[90] Nartea A, Kuhalskaya A, Fanesi B, Orhotohwo OL, Susek K, Rocchetti L, Di Vittori V, Bitocchi E, Pacetti D, Papa R. Legume byproducts as ingredients for food applications: Preparation, nutrition, bioactivity, and techno-functional properties. Comprehensive Reviews in Food Science and Food Safety. 2023;**22**(3):1953–1985. DOI: 10.1111/1541-4337.13137

[91] Foschia M, Horstmann SW, Arendt EK, Zannini E. Legumes as functional ingredients in gluten-free bakery and pasta products. Annual Review of Food Science and Technology. 2017;**8**(1):75–96. DOI: 10.1146/annurev-food-030216-030045

[92] Benevides CMDJ, Trindade BA, Lopes MV. Potentialities of legumes in the pharmaceutical industry. Journal of Analytical & Pharmaceutical Research.

2018;7(3):369–373. DOI: 10.15406/japlr.2018.07.00253

[93] Morris B. Bio-functional legumes with nutraceutical, pharmaceutical, and industrial uses. Economic Botany. 2003;57:254–261. DOI: 10.1663/0013-0001(2003)057[0254:BLWNPA]2.0.CO;2

[94] González-Montoya M, Cano-Sampedro E, Mora-Escobedo R. Bioactive peptides from legumes as anticancer therapeutic agents. International Journal of Cancer and Clinical Research. 2017;**4**(2). DOI: 10.23937/2378-3419/1410081

[95] Kapoor S. Bioactive and Therapeutic Potential of Legumes: A review. International Journal of Pharmacy and Biological Sciences. 2015;**5**(2):65–74

[96] Nikkhah A. Legumes as Medicine: Nature Prescribes. Iran: Medicinal & Aromatic Plants; 2014

[97] Rubio LA, Molina E. Las leguminosas en alimentación animal. Arbor. 2016;**192**(779):a315. DOI: 10.3989/arbor.2016.779n3005

[98] Phelan P, Moloney AP, McGeough EJ, Humphreys J, Bertilsson J, O'Riordan EG, O'Kiely P. Forage legumes for grazing and conserving in ruminant production systems. Critical Reviews in Plant Sciences. 2015; **34**(1–3):281–326. DOI: 10.1080/07352689.2014.898455

[99] Lüscher A, Mueller-Harvey I, Soussana JF, Rees RM, Peyraud JL. Potential of legume-based grassland–livestock systems in Europe: A review. Grass and Forage Science. 2014;**69**(2):206–228. DOI: 10.1111/gfs.12124

[100] Nandi T, Menon S, Das S. Impact of micro-nutrients on growth and development of fodder crops under water stress condition: A review. International Journal of Plant & Soil Science. 2024;**36**(5):989–999. DOI: 10.9734/ijpss/2024/v36i54595

[101] Mohanta RK, Garg AK. Organic Trace Minerals: Immunity, Health, Production and Reproduction in Farm Animals. Indian Journal of Animal Nutrition. 2014;**31**(3):203–212

[102] Saripinar-Aksu D, Aksu T, Ercüment Önel S. Does inclusion at low levels of organically complexed minerals versus inorganic forms create a weakness in performance or antioxidant defense system in broiler diets? International Journal of Poultry Science. 2012;**11**(10):666–672. DOI: 10.3923/ijps.2012.666.672

[103] Uniyal S, Dutta N, Raza M, Jaiswal SK, Sahoo JK, Ashwin K. Application of nano minerals in the field of animal nutrition: A review. Bulletin of Environment, Pharmacology and Life Sciences. 2017;**6**(4):4–8. DOI: 10.1080/23311932.2023.2290308

[104] Oladejo EO, Ogunkunle NF. The roles of dietary organic trace minerals on animal antioxidative status, gut health, and environmental sustainability: A review. Journal of Agricultural Science. 2024;**17**(1):37. DOI: 10.5539/jas.v17n1p37

[105] Sandberg A-S. Bioavailability of minerals in legumes. British Journal of Nutrition. 2002;**88**(S3):281–285. DOI: 10.1079/BJN/2002718

[106] Urbano G, López-Jurado M, Aranda P, Vidal-Valverde C, Tenorio E, Porres J. The role of phytic acid in legumes: Antinutrient or beneficial

function? Journal of Physiology and Biochemistry. 2000;**56**(3):283–294. DOI: 10.1007/BF03179796

[107] Chitra U, Singh U, Venkateswara Rao P. Phytic acid, in vitro protein digestibility, dietary fiber, and minerals of pulses as influenced by processing methods. Plant Foods for Human Nutrition. 1996;**49**(4):307–316. DOI: 10.1007/BF01091980

[108] Nsabimana S, Ismail T, Lazarte CE. Enhancing iron and zinc bioavailability in maize (Zea mays) through phytate reduction: The impact of fermentation alone and in combination with soaking and germination. Frontiers in Nutrition. 2024;11. DOI: 10.3389/fnut.2024.1478155

[109] Provenza FD. What does it mean to be locally adapted and who cares anyway? Journal of Animal Science. 2008;**86**(suppl_14):E271–E284. DOI: 10.2527/jas.2007-0468

[110] Fisher GEJ.Micronutrients and animal nutrition and the link between the application of micronutrients to crops and animal health. Turkish Journal of Agriculture and Forestry. 2008;**32**(3):221–233

[111] Jakobsen K, Hermansen J. Organic farming – A challenge to nutritionists. Journal of Animal and Feed Sciences. 2001;**10**(Suppl. 1):29–42. DOI: 10.22358/jafs/70010/2001

[112] Lal R. Enhancing eco-efficiency in agro-ecosystems through soil carbon sequestration. Crop Science. 2010;**50**(S1). DOI: 10.2135/cropsci2010.01.0012

[113] Papendick RI, Parr JF. Soil quality —The key to a sustainable agriculture. American Journal of Alternative Agriculture. 1992;**7**(1–2):2–3. DOI: 10.1017/S0889189300004343

[114] European Parliament and Council of the European Union. Regulation (EU) 2021/2115 of the European Parliament and of the Council of 2 December 2021 establishing rules on support for strategic plans to be drawn up by Member States under the common agricultural policy (CAP Strategic Plans) and financed by the European Agricultural Guarantee Fund (EAGF) and by the European Agricultural Fund for Rural Development (EAFRD[EG1]) and repealing Regulations (EU) No 1305/2013 and (EU) No 1307/2013. Official Journal of the European Union. 2021. https://eur-lex.europa.eu/eli/reg/2021/2115/2024-05-25

[115] Imran A, Hussain I, Ali I, Ullah S, Iqbal A, Al-Tawaha AR, Al-Tawaha AR, Thangadurai D, Sangeetha J, Rauf A, Saranraj P, Al Sultan W, AL-Taey DKA, Youssef RA, Sirajuddin SN. Agricultural soil reclamation and restoration of soil organic matter and nutrients via application of organic, inorganic and bio fertilization (Mini review). IOP Conference Series: Earth and Environmental Science. 2021; **788**(1):012165. DOI: 10.1088/1755-1315/788/1/012165

[116] Lal R. Restoring soil quality to mitigate soil degradation. Sustainability. 2015;**7**(5):5875–5895. DOI: 10.3390/su7055875

[117] Neuenkamp L, García de León D, Hamer U, Hölzel N, McGale E, Hannula SE. Comprehensive tools for ecological restoration of soils foster sustainable use and resilience of agricultural land. Communications Biology. 2024;**7**(1):1577. DOI: 10.1038/s42003-024-07275-2

[118] Vanghele N-A, Vladut N-V, Pruteanu A, Matache A, Vladutoiu L-C, Vrânceanu N-O. Novel solutions for mitigating drought impact and restoring soil functionality in agriculture. INMATEH Agricultural Engineering. 2025;1352–1381. DOI: 10.35633/inmateh-76-112

[119] Mrunalini K, Behera B, Jayaraman S, Abhilash PC, Dubey PK, Swamy GN, Prasad JVNS, Rao KV, Krishnan P, Pratibha G, Srinivasa Rao C. Nature-based solutions in soil restoration for improving agricultural productivity. Land Degradation & Development. 2022;**33**(8):1269–1289. DOI: 10.1002/ldr.4207

[120] Pérez-Jaramillo JE, de Hollander M, Ramírez CA, Mendes R, Raaijmakers JM, Carrión VJ. Deciphering rhizosphere microbiome assembly of wild and modern common bean (Phaseolus vulgaris) in native and agricultural soils from Colombia. Microbiome. 2019;**7**(1):114. DOI: 10.1186/s40168-019-0727-1

[121] Gupta R, Anand G, Gaur R, Yadav D. Plant–microbiome interactions for sustainable agriculture: A review. Physiology and Molecular Biology of Plants. 2021;**27**(1):165–179. DOI: 10.1007/s12298-021-00927-1

[122] Porter SS, Sachs JL. Agriculture and the disruption of plant–microbial symbiosis. Trends in Ecology & Evolution. 2020;**35**(5):426–439. DOI: 10.1016/j.tree.2020.01.006

[123] Khande R, Sharma SK, Ramesh A, Sharma MP. Zinc solubilizing Bacillus strains that modulate growth, yield and zinc biofortification of soybean and wheat. Rhizosphere. 2017;**4**:126–138. DOI: 10.1016/j.rhisph.2017.09.002

Chapter 4

Global Legume Production, Constraints and Future Prospects

Aggrey Keya Osogo

Abstract

Fabaceae is the third-largest family of flowering plants, with over 800 genera and about 23,000 species. Around 20 species are consumed by humans. They are known for their high protein, fiber, and carbohydrate content, as well as their low fat levels. Common beans, chickpeas, lentils, broad beans, cowpeas, and peas are the most widely cultivated and used as food crops. Compared with cereals, they contain two to three times as much protein. The common bean has the largest share of global consumption. Legumes are a staple diet in the Mediterranean and are also used as forage and livestock feed. Despite their nutritional and health benefits, legume yields remain below their potential due to abiotic, genetic, socioeconomic, environmental, and institutional constraints. This chapter examines these challenges and emphasizes the importance of adopting cutting-edge breeding technologies to develop climate-smart varieties and integrated disease and pest management approaches. These strategies can enhance food security and reduce child malnutrition.

Keywords: legumes, production constraints, production potential, nutritional health benefits, Fabaceae

1. Introduction

Legumes (family Fabaceae) are the flowering plants that include some of the most diverse and economically important groups. The family comprises over 800 genera and approximately 23,000 species [1]. Twenty species are cultivated, consumed, and utilized worldwide for food and nutrition security. Legumes are known to contain high levels of protein, complex carbohydrates, dietary fiber, and essential minerals, while typically having low fat content. Among the most widely cultivated species are common beans, cowpeas, chickpeas, lentils, soybeans, groundnuts, and peas. Through symbiotic associations with rhizobia, legumes fix atmospheric nitrogen, thereby improving soil fertility and reducing dependence on synthetic fertilizers [2].

Millions of smallholder farmers globally depend on legumes for their livelihoods. In marginal settings, legumes enhance and promote the sustainability of farming methods, for instance, crop rotations, intercropping systems, and sustainable land management practices. Despite these benefits, worldwide production of legumes remains comparatively low compared to other crops, such as, cereals and oilseeds. There is a large gap between the global potential for legume production and the yields realized by farmers in the field. On-farm legume yields are often less than half of their potential. Studies have shown that in some regions, for instance, sub-Saharan Africa (SSA), yields may reach about 25% of the water-limited yield potential (Yw) [3]. Legume yields have either remained constant or declined in many regions due to a combination of biotic [4], abiotic [5], socioeconomic [6], and institutional constraints [7].

Viral, bacterial, and fungal diseases, insect pests, and parasitic weeds are the main biotic challenges that limit production. In Africa and South Asia, abiotic stresses, including drought, heat, soil salinity, and nutrient shortages, have further aggravated yield losses. Studies have shown that in some legumes, instances of 100% yield losses have been reported as a result of these diseases [8]. Besides biotic and abiotic factors, there are also socioeconomic barriers, such as limited access to quality seed, inadequate extension services, poor infrastructure, weak value chains, and volatile market prices. This situation has been worsened by climate change, which has altered rainfall patterns, pest behavior, and geographic spread, thereby escalating production challenges [9].

The current understanding of legume physiology, resistance mechanisms, and pathways has been brought about by new developments in genomics, transcriptomics, and metabolomics research. Top-of-the-art breeding techniques, including marker-assisted selection, genomic selection, and genome editing, have made it possible to develop high-yielding, climate-ready, and pest-resistant varieties [10]. The production of legumes can be enhanced while preserving ecosystem integrity and stability through improvements in agronomic management, such as, precision agriculture, biofertilizers, and conservation tillage [11]. Policy shifts toward sustainable agriculture and plant-based diets have had a positive impact and placed legumes at the center of global food systems [12].

This chapter, *"Global Legume Production, Constraints, and Future Prospects,"* incorporates an elaborate global multidisciplinary method that analyzes the current state of legume cultivation and production. It identifies the constraints that limit production while, at the same time, reevaluates production trends across continents. The role of legumes in meeting future food and nutritional requirements has been examined. Approaches that could unlock the full yield potential of legumes are explored. Topics such as a global overview of legume production, the significance of legumes, the global production status of legumes, constraints to legume production, advances and opportunities in legume production, research and development (R&D) priorities and future prospects, and policy directions in legume production have been covered. Sustainable pathways for the improvement of legumes have been identified to address the current production challenges. Researchers, agricultural practitioners, policymakers, and development partners will greatly benefit from this volume. Improvement of legume production systems will not only address global food security and environmental resilience but also nurture the planet.

2. Global overview of legume production

2.1 Key legumes and regions

Soybeans, common beans, chickpeas, peas, lentils, peanuts, and cowpeas are the widely cultivated legumes (**Table 1**). These legumes have the ability to fix atmospheric nitrogen through biological nitrogen fixation (BNF). As a result, they play a crucial role in human nutrition, animal feed production, and help improve soil fertility.

Legume	Common names	Distribution	Importance
Soybeans (*Glycine max*)		Worldwide	Food, animal feed, and oil extraction
Common beans (*Phaseolus vulgaris*)	Kidney, pinto, navy, and black beans	Worldwide	Human consumption as a source of dietary proteins
Peanuts (*Arachis hypogaea*)	Groundnuts	Worldwide	Food and oil
Peas (*Pisum sativum*)	Garden peas, English peas, shelling peas, and pulses	Worldwide	Fresh consumption (as a vegetable) and as dry peas (a pulse crop)
Chickpeas (*Cicer arietinum*)	Garbanzo beans	Middle East and South Asia	
Lentils (*Lens culinaris*)	Dal (a generic Hindi term), Masoor dal for red lentils, and Chana dal for Bengal gram	South Asian	Edible, lens-shaped seeds
Cowpeas (*Vigna unguiculata*)	Black-eyed pea, Southern pea, crowder pea, field pea, catjang (or catjang cowpea), asparagus bean, yard-long bean (or Chinese long bean), and pea bean	Africa and Asia	Protein-rich food and animal feed
Broad beans (*Vicia faba*)	Fava beans	In China, North Africa, and the Mediterranean basin	Health and nutritional, ecological and agricultural, cultural, and historical importance
Pigeon peas (*Cajanus cajan*)	Red gram, Congo pea (English), gandules (Spanish), pois d'Angole (French), and arhar (Hindi)	Indian subcontinent and other tropical/subtropical regions	Nutritional and digestive benefits, as well as regulation of the heart and blood sugar.
Lupins (*Lupinus spp.*)	Blue lupin (*Lupinus angustifolius*) and white lupin (L. *albus*), Andean lupin or tarwi (*L. mutabilis*), and sky lupin (*L. nanus*)	Europe, the Mediterranean region, and the Andean region	Food and animal feed
Alfalfa (*Medicago sativa*)	Lucerne, buffalo herb, purple medick, and snail clover	Globally, including Central Asia, Central Europe, Northern Africa, North America, and parts of Australia	Livestock feed
Clover (*Trifolium spp.*)	White clover (*Trifolium repens*): Dutch clover, ladino clover, and white Dutch clover	Cosmopolitan distribution, including Europe and Central Asia, North America, Australia and New Zealand, Africa, South America, and Asia (Western and Northern)	Forage crop

Table 1.
Types of legumes, distribution, and importance.

2.2 Global production status of legumes

Legume production has increased over the decades, driven by expanded cultivation areas and improved yields. Major legumes such as, soybean, chickpea, and lentils play a significant role in food security and sustainable agriculture. The combined production of key legumes increased by 548.6% from 1961 to 2016, with a remarkable annual growth rate of 3.5% [13]. Conversely, worldwide production of common beans and other legumes has continued to increase, albeit variably, from 2000 to 2025 (**Figure 1**). The common bean is one of the most important legumes and is grown in all continents (**Figure 2**).

Long-term production of most legumes reflects both horizontal expansion and modest productivity improvement rather than uniform yield breakthroughs. For instance, pulse yields are substantially less than cereals (global pulse yield ~ 0.989 t ha^{-1} vs. cereals ~ 4.179 t ha^{-1} in 2022) [14]. In the tropics, legume production is concentrated in SSA and South Asia, where it holds major social and economic importance for millions of smallholders [15]. There are substantial efforts to raise legume output by closing yield gaps with improved varieties, better agronomy, and cropping system changes. Several studies show wide variability in attainable yields across species and environments. A global experimental compilation covering 39 grain-legume species reported yields, biomass, and management effects across five continents, providing the basis for identifying higher-performing species and management packages [16]. Regional yield-gap studies (e.g., Ethiopia) show meaningful water-limited yield potentials and sizable yield gaps that, if closed, would increase regional output substantially [17].

The global average actual yields for pulses are low, around 900–950 kg/ha in the recent past. This contrasts sharply with average yields for cereals (e.g., maize, wheat, and rice), which are significantly higher (e.g., maize at 5.97 t/ha, or 5970 kg/ha) [18]. In studies conducted in East Africa, actual yields were found to be only 15% in Kenya, 23% in Tanzania, and 41% in Ethiopia of the water-limited potential (Yw) [19]. The yield deficit in legumes is mostly larger than in cereals; average actual yields for legumes are often 41% lower than on-station trial yields and 69% lower than the highest experimental yields [17]. The significant gap between possible and real yields from these legumes results from a mixture of genetic, environmental, technological, and socioeconomic factors.

3. Significance of legumes

3.1 BNF and intercropping system

Legumes, through the process of nitrogen fixation, improve soil properties. They help raise successive crop yields by playing key roles in crop rotations and intercropping. Through the process of BNF, legumes can improve crop nutrition and the soil health system, which in turn meets most of the nitrogen requirements. In studies based on legume species and management in a single season, approximately 80–90% of the crop's nitrogen demand was fixed, and 0–70% of the nitrogen was transferred to subsequent crops [20]. Integration of cereal grains or pulse legumes during crop rotation has been shown to improve the yields of subsequent cereal crops. Similarly, studies conducted in Morocco on the crop rotation of faba beans and

DOI: http://dx.doi.org/10.5772/intechopen.1015042

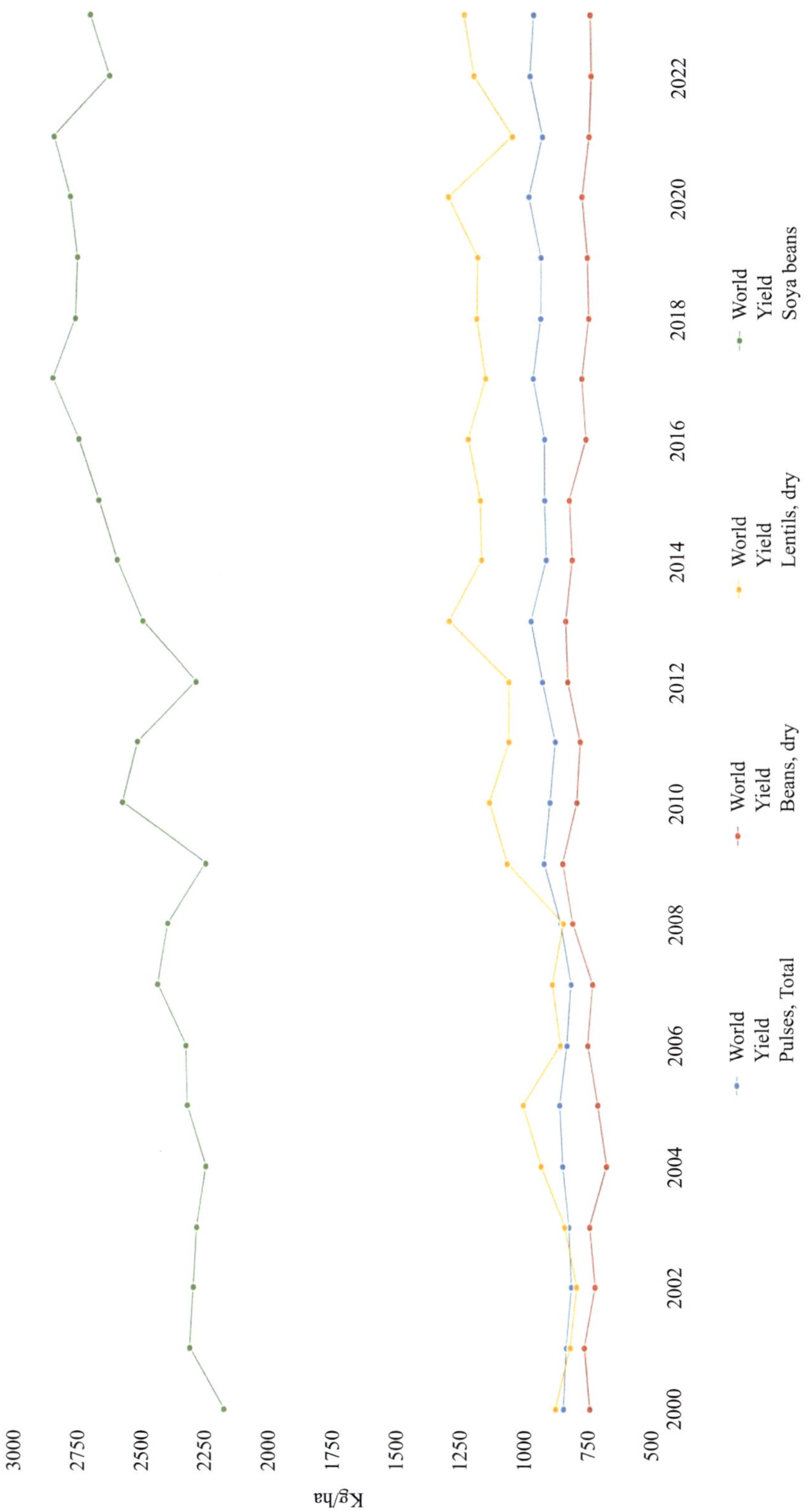

Figure 1.
Selected legumes' yield in kg/ha from 2000 to 2025.

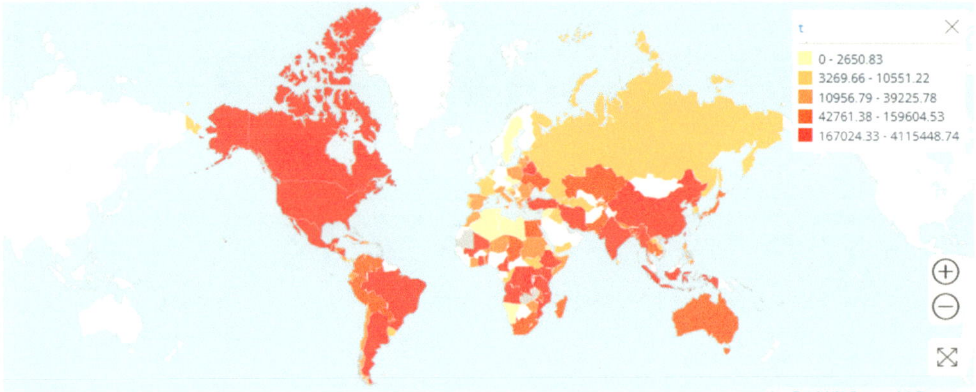

Figure 2.
Common bean-producing areas in tonnage worldwide.

wheat cultivation yielded elevated two-year gross margins of US$537 per hectare, which represented a 48% increase compared to a system of continuous wheat cultivation [21]. Leguminous crops have long been utilized to improve resource acquisition and promote overall soil health. Apart from mitigating the occurrence of weeds and pests, legumes augmented cereal yields by 15–25% while at the same time maintaining soil integrity and water resources [22]. Forage legumes enhance forage quality and yield stability, reducing the need for artificial nitrogen inputs in livestock systems, thereby decreasing reliance on procured protein feed [23]. Selecting varieties and species appropriate for local climatic conditions and implementing proper pest and disease management are required to effectively integrate legumes into cropping systems [24]. To ensure optimal residue incorporation, careful assessment of benefits at the crop rotation level is critical rather than focusing solely on single-crop performance criteria [25].

3.2 Global nutrition and food security

Leguminous crops influence farm profitability, market supply chains, national protein balances, and trade. Their economics vary depending on product type, region, and management [26]. Higher gross margins have been realized for legume-cereal rotations in several settings. Previous studies carried out in Finland demonstrated that faba bean-based rotations had positive long-term implications for soil quality and biodiversity [27]. Although Europe cultivates only a small share of the world's grain-legume area, it relies heavily on protein feed imports – approximately 20 million tonnes of soybean meal and 12 million tonnes of soybean grain annually [28]. However, this dependence restricts regional protein self-sufficiency while, at the same time, offering a significant market opportunity to increase domestic legume production. Legumes minimize fertilizer costs, expenses, and emissions through an economic-environment trade-off. This decreases grain-legume gross margins in some regions [29], while forage legumes improve margins in others. Identifying locally profitable legume systems requires region-specific management and advisory engagement [8]. Income generation from legume adoption raises system yields, decreases purchased nitrogen inputs, and supplies marketable grain or high-value forage for resource-poor farm families [30].

3.3 Human nutrition and livestock nutrition

Legumes are rich in protein and micronutrients and contribute directly to quality diets and indirectly to food security through resilient production systems. They provide 20–45% protein, with ~ 60% complex carbohydrates and 5–37% dietary fiber. They contain essential amino acids, minerals, vitamins, and are low in cholesterol [31]. Legume consumption is also implicated in the prevention of malnutrition and forms the basis of affordable, plant-based protein solutions and functional foods for vulnerable groups [32]. Past evaluations and studies have proposed that substantial increases in legume seed availability (e.g., ~ 60 g seed per person per day) would be required to meet older target protein/energy consumption yardsticks in many regions [33]. By increasing on-farm protein production and reducing dependency on imported protein meals, legume expansion strengthens and supports national food security and supply-chain resilience [11].

Legumes play a pivotal role in livestock feeding systems by providing high-quality and often low-cost protein, energy, and essential minerals, while at the same time improving soil fertility through BNF. Forage and grain legumes complement cereals and pastures by enhancing diet quality and feed autonomy [34]. Forage legumes, such as alfalfa, provide highly digestible protein and minerals for ruminants, while grain legumes can partially replace imported soybean meal in monogastric diets when properly processed [35]. Although antinutritional factors limit direct use, appropriate thermal or mechanical processing mitigates these effects. Overall, legumes enhance animal productivity, reduce feed costs and imports, and support sustainable, environmentally resilient livestock systems [36].

3.4 Soil structure improvement, carbon sequestration, and crop rotation

Legumes, when integrated into local cropping systems, have the effect of reducing dependence on synthetic nitrogen and greenhouse gas emissions. The rise in cropping system resilience under stress can be enhanced by soil organic matter and water relations [8]. Research has shown that cropping systems integrating legumes can reduce nitrogen fertilizer use by approximately 24% (arable) and 38% (forage), while cutting N_2O emissions by about 18% (arable) and 33% (forage) on average [37]. Studies in Europe have demonstrated lower ecological footprints and benefits to soil organic carbon (SOC) [38]. The growth of legumes has significantly reduced the demand for fossil fuel-derived nitrogen fertilizers. When incorporated into diversified cropping systems, legumes can contribute to SOC build-up and reduce the agricultural ecological footprint [39]. Pest and disease cycles can be broken, weeds subdued through canopy effects, soil water retention enhanced, nutrient cycling improved, and thereby boost system resilience to climate when legumes are intercropped and diversified with other crops [40]. These environmental gains depend on species, management, and regional conditions; in some regions, certain grain-legume introductions may lower farm gross margins. Therefore, codesigning management practices and value chains is essential to achieving both environmental and economic benefits.

4. Constraints to legume production

4.1 Biophysical and environmental constraints in legume production

Legume production faces various biophysical and environmental factors that limit plant growth, BNF, and yield. Abiotic stresses are the most common challenges in legume-growing regions. Drought reduces photosynthesis, hampers nodulation, and can decrease BNF by 30–80%, especially in crops such as, common bean, chickpea, and cowpea [41]. Heat stress, which is becoming more frequent with climate change, damages pollen viability, accelerates aging, and lowers seed set [42].

Waterlogging and flooding are implicated in the reduction of oxygen availability in roots, slowing rhizobial activity and enhancing the risk of root rot infections [43]. Salinity and sodicity impair seed germination and vegetative growth, with sensitive legumes such as, chickpea and common bean experiencing substantial yield declines at moderate salinity levels [23]. Nutrient disparities, especially deficiencies in phosphorus, sulfur, molybdenum, iron, and zinc, hinder nodule formation and nitrogenase activity. Acidic soils often cause aluminum toxicity and hinder root development [44].

4.2 Biotic constraints

Biotic stressors apply extra and often synergistic pressure. Important insect pests, including bean fly, pod borers, aphids, whiteflies, cutworms, bruchid beetles, and nematodes (**Table 2**), cause severe pre and postharvest losses and act as vectors of viral diseases. Major diseases such as, Ascochyta blight, anthracnose, Fusarium wilt, rusts, bacterial blights, and viruses such as, bean common mosaic virus (BCMV) and Cowpea aphid-borne mosaic virus (CABMV) (**Figure 3**) reduce yields and stability in both temperate and tropical production systems [45]. Legumes often compete with parasitic weeds such as, Striga and *Alectra* spp. for nutrients and impose substantial productivity consequences, especially in SSA [46]. Besides these challenges are soil fertility problems that are prevalent in smallholder and rain-fed systems. Reduced levels of phosphorus availability in soils have been implicated in the restriction of ATP generation required for BNF, thus reducing nitrogen fixation by more than half [47]. Reduced moisture retention, aeration, and microbial activity weaken root growth and symbiotic effectiveness in soils with poor organic matter. Native rhizobia that are less effective outcompete inoculant strains, occasioning poor nodulation and nitrogen fixation in high-temperature, acidity, or drought stress conditions [48].

4.3 Abiotic constraints

Elevated temperature extremes, intensified rainfall variability, and alteration of pest and pathogen dynamics as a result of climate change have worsened these production challenges [49]. Heat waves during flowering are becoming more frequent, leading to widespread flower abortion and reduced seed filling [50]. Greater rainfall variability is contributing to planting delays, midseason droughts, and episodic flooding, each of these with substantial impacts on legume physiology

Pests	Causal agent	Affected legumes	Key symptoms	Management practices
Aphids	*Aphis* spp.	Bean, cowpea, soybean, chickpea	Leaf curling, stunting, honeydew, and virus transmission	Use resistant varieties; promote natural enemies, such as, ladybirds and parasitoids; apply selective insecticides, such as, pymetrozine and flonicamid, when thresholds are exceeded; and use reflective mulches.
Bean fly	*Ophiomyia* spp.	Common bean	Stem swelling, cracking near the soil line, and plant death	Early planting, resistant varieties, seed dressing with imidacloprid or thiamethoxam, hilling up, and field sanitation.
Pod borer	*Maruca vitrata*	Cowpea, bean	Flower webbing, pod damage, and larval feeding	Use pheromone traps; Bt formulations; resistant cowpea lines; neem extracts; and timely insecticide sprays (lambda-cyhalothrin).
Leaf beetles/ bruchids	*Ootheca* spp.	Common bean	Small circular holes, defoliation	Crop rotation, early planting, botanical pesticides, and soil amendments to improve vigor.
Thrips	*Thrips tabaci,* Megalurothrips sjostedti	Bean, cowpea	Silvering leaves, flower shedding	Early planting, resistant cultivars, blue sticky traps, avoiding continuous cropping, and using insecticides only at flowering if necessary.
Whiteflies	*Bemisia tabaci*	Beans, soybean	Yellowing, sooty mold, and virus transmission.	Use virus-free seed, reflective mulching, biological control, systemic insecticides in severe outbreaks, and weed control.
Root-knot nematodes	*Meloidogyne* spp.	Bean, soybean, groundnut	Root galls, stunting, and reduced nodulation.	Rotate with cereals; use resistant or tolerant varieties; apply organic amendments; utilize nematicide seed treatments; and practice solarization in nurseries.
Cutworms/ armyworms	*Spodoptera* spp.	All legumes	Defoliation, stem cutting, and rapid canopy destruction	Scouting; pheromone traps; conservation of natural enemies; early planting; strategic insecticide application if thresholds are reached.
Termites	Various spp.	Groundnut, soybean	Plant wilting, tunneling, and lodging	Destroy mounds; apply soil treatments (use chlorpyrifos alternatives where permitted); maintain soil moisture; manage crop residue.

Table 2.
Major pests of legumes, their symptoms, and management practices.

and BNF. Although elevated CO_2 can marginally enhance photosynthesis, it generally fails to compensate for the negative effects of heat, drought, and nutrient limitations. Production systems are being threatened by global warming through the geographical expansion of insect pests and pathogens [51]. Addressing these limitations requires integrated strategies that combine stress-tolerant varieties, improved soil fertility and rhizobia management, effective pest and disease control, and climate-adaptive agronomic practices.

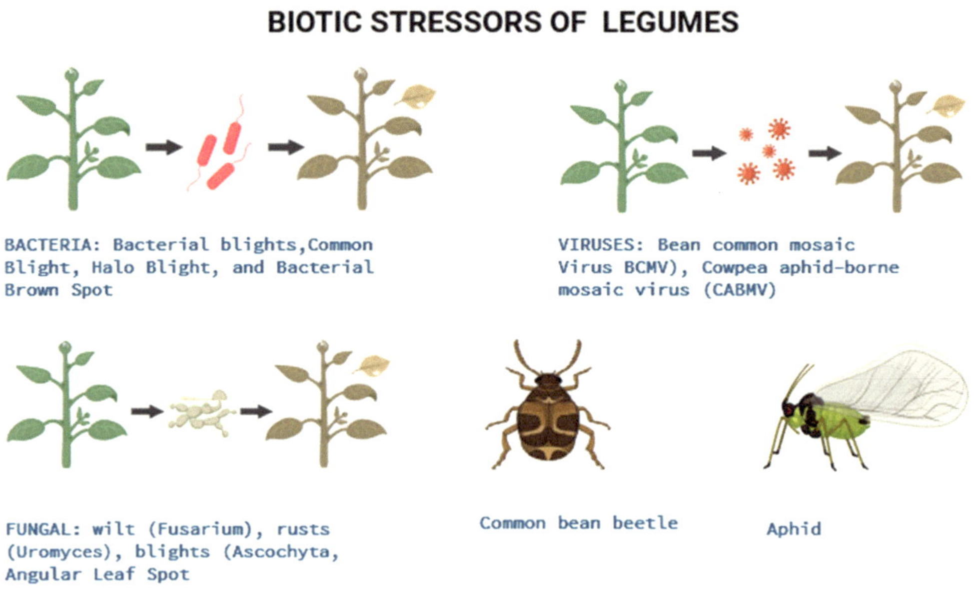

Figure 3.
Biotic factors limiting legume production worldwide.

4.4 Genetic and agronomic limitations

A blend of genetic, technological, breeding, and agronomic factors limits legume improvement globally, collectively slowing genetic gain and reducing productivity. Genetic diversity within domesticated legume gene pools and the limited use of crop wild relatives, resulting from historical bottlenecks, is the greatest setback [52]. Low levels of polymorphism, which restrict allele discovery and the effectiveness of marker-assisted selection, are prevalent in many legumes [53]. Most legume varieties are susceptible to pests, diseases, and climate stress due to their closeness and similarities [17]. Valuable adaptive traits from wild relatives are often hindered by reproductive barriers, linkage drag, and inadequate conservation and prebreeding efforts.

Irregular development and availability of genomics and phenotyping resources have impeded progress. Many grain legumes and minor pulses lack comprehensive markers, maps, and high-resolution genomic platforms, even though some major legumes benefit from reference genomes and molecular tools [54]. Genomic technologies restrict their routine application, particularly in resource-poor breeding programs, due to the high costs involved. Low-throughput and imprecise phenotyping is a major hindrance that weakens genotype–phenotype associations and delays the translation of genomic advances into improved varieties [55]. There is low investment in genomics and molecular breeding of neglected and underutilized pulses.

Legume improvement, breeding, and rebreeding are often slowed by constraints. Yield, drought tolerance, and nutrient-use efficiency are quantitatively inherited and often show low to moderate heritability [56]. Long breeding cycles, limited selection intensity, and the need for extensive prebreeding to introgress wild alleles further reduce rates of genetic gain [57]. Multitrait breeding objectives, including stress tolerance, seed quality, nitrogen fixation efficiency, and system compatibility, raise phenotyping costs and operational complexity [58].

Production of legumes in rainfed smallholder systems is particularly hampered by agronomic and cultivation constraints. Drought, heat, salinity, pests, and diseases cause major yield losses, which are aggravated by changes in climatic conditions [59]. Lower productivity compared with cereals reduces farmer incentives, while limited access to quality seed, inputs, and tailored agronomic packages constrains adoption. These challenges are especially acute for neglected legumes, where reliance on landraces and weak institutional support further impedes improvement [59].

4.5 Socioeconomic, institutional, and value chain constraints

Socioeconomic and institutional factors heavily impact the potential for legume production to improve nutrition, soil health, and smallholder incomes. The main obstacles in this regard are policy and market limitations. Numerous agricultural strategies have, for a long time, favored staple cereals in many low- and middle-income countries [60]. Many studies, research efforts, extension support, and subsidies are primarily channeled toward cereals. Without significant public investment and attention, legumes remain orphaned and unexplored. Legume producers often face unstable, fragmented markets, especially in the absence of the creation of effective policies and price support systems. Transaction costs in output markets remain relatively high. These smallholder farmers, equipped with limited bargaining power, are left vulnerable to exploitation and price fluctuations. For instance, studies on smallholder legume farmers in Malawi have demonstrated that farmers struggle with systems characterized by urban-biased price controls, high intermediary costs, and insecure contract arrangements [18]. In addition, credit limitations, poor infrastructure, and misinformation negatively impact input and output markets [61].

Most smallholder legume farmers rely on saved seed, local markets, or exchanges as sources of seed rather than formal supply systems. These seed systems are weak or underdeveloped and out of reach for farmers. A recent study in SSA showed that up to 90% of legume seed sown by smallholders comes from the informal sector [3]. The formal seed supply chain is considered inconsistent, costly, and out of reach for most remote farmers. Formal seed systems are plagued by low profit and returns; for instance, legume seeds often have low viability (e.g., groundnut and cowpea), making them unattractive to private seed companies [3]. Many regulatory frameworks in various countries do not favor or recognize informal seed systems. Seed laws and certification often emphasize formal systems [19]. This has created a gap for community networks. Seeds and other inputs such as, rhizobium inoculants, fertilizers, and crop protection are not always available, suitable, or affordable for smallholders. As a result, the full potential of legume crops cannot be realized [62].

Women often take lead roles in legume cultivation and postharvest handling, yet have less secure access to land, credit, extension services, and markets. Studies in Malawi, for instance, show a productivity gap between men and women legume producers [63]. This is partly due to unequal access to productive inputs and time constraints stemming from childcare and household responsibilities. Labor is another major obstacle, where, for instance, intensive labor is required during planting, weeding, and harvesting of legumes. Smallholder households normally experience labor shortages or time constraints, especially when family members migrate or are occupied with nonfarming activities. Many smallholder farmers are not risk-takers. Their farm sizes are predominantly small, assets are limited, and they often lack access to credit. Farmers often prefer not to expand legume cultivation despite its long-term advantages since legume returns can be variable or less than those of staple cereals. Postharvest losses are prevalent. Farmers lack proper drying, storage, and sorting facilities, leading to pest damage and weight loss. In the absence of aggregation centers, farmers frequently pay high costs to transport produce to market [18]. Value-chain players, including processors, aggregators, and exporters, are often weak or absent, and with poor contract enforcement systems [64] further exacerbate the issue. This discourages farmers from investing heavily in legumes due to the inability to sell into stable and remunerative markets. Infrastructure deficiencies, poor road networks, and limited storage exacerbate this situation, raising transaction costs and significantly reducing farm-gate incentives. In conclusion, the production of legumes is impacted by deep social and institutional structures entrenched in our societies. All major players in the legume industry, including policymakers, donors, and private actors, must jointly coordinate to strengthen seed systems, improve market infrastructure, and address labor and gender inequities. Without such efforts, the full promise of legumes in food security, nutrition, and sustainable farming will not be met.

5. Advances and opportunities in legume production

5.1 Advances in breeding and biotechnology

Global legume food systems have opened new opportunities and achieved major improvements in productivity, resilience, and sustainability. High-yielding, stress-tolerant, and market-preferred varieties have been developed using modern breeding techniques [65]. Through techniques in genomic selection, pangenomics, high-throughput phenotyping, and gene editing, such as clustered regularly interspaced short palindromic repeats (CRISPR)/Cas9, the accuracy and speed of breeding pipelines have been enhanced [66]. The bottlenecks previously encountered in legume transformation and regeneration have been overcome through innovations in transformation protocols. Breeding methods have been refined and enhanced by the use of tissue culture techniques. Using next-generation sequencing and omics technologies, new insights into genetic variation have been uncovered. Crop yields and productivity under various stress conditions, such as, drought and heat, can be improved by adopting a seed-resilient system [67]. These technologies have enabled breeders to integrate numerous traits, such as, drought tolerance, nitrogen fixation efficiency, pest and disease resistance, and enhanced nutritional quality. Novel diversity from wild relatives is now being utilized in many legume breeding programs to address climate-related and biotic challenges.

5.2 Microbial and biological inputs

Biofertilizers and plant-associated microbiomes are increasingly being applied to enhance legume yield, soil fertility, and genetic advancements [42]. Biological nitrogen fixation remains a major benefit of legumes. Recent studies have demonstrated numerous opportunities for enhancing BNF through improved rhizobia inoculants, the usage of plant growth-promoting bacteria, and formulation technologies [43]. Enhancing microbial survival and root colonization, stress resilience, and reducing fertilizer reliance is now possible through the application of endophytes and synthetic microbial consortia [68]. Advances in microencapsulation, carrier materials, and soil-specific strains have improved the effectiveness and adoption of biologically-based inputs.

5.3 Precision agriculture and digital technologies

Precision agriculture and digital technologies have made it possible to make real-time decisions and optimize the limited resources available. By using tools such as, remote sensing, soil sensors, drones, and satellite-based analytics, timely interventions in planting, fertilization, irrigation, and pest control can be made [44]. Forecasting disease outbreaks and identifying nutrient deficiencies using machine-learning models is transforming farming. In addition, these models can optimize plant populations for site-specific conditions. Digital platforms can be utilized to enhance farmer access to advisory services, markets, and weather information [69]. To include more accurate phenotypic data and enhance selection effectiveness, automated data collection in breeding programs has been adopted.

5.4 Integration of all the techniques

Integration of legumes into sustainable cropping systems offers opportunities for establishing climate-smart and regenerative agricultural landscapes. Improvement of soil health can be enhanced by nitrogen fixation, organic matter build-up, and improved soil structure, while at the same time supporting diversified rotations that break pest and disease cycles. Intercropping legumes with cereals, conservation agriculture, and using them as cover crops or forages has the capacity to enhance agroecosystems, minimizing dependence on synthetic fertilizers and improving carbon sequestration [70]. Smallholder systems stand to benefit more from this function in sustainable intensification. Microbial technologies, digital innovations, modern breeding techniques, and sustainable system integration place legumes as foundation crops for future food security, ecological stability, and climate resilience.

5.5 Agronomic and crop management strategies

Legume agronomy combines low-input practices to improve yields, soil fertility, and system resilience. Maintaining soil organic matter, amending soil pH, ensuring adequate phosphorus, and applying rhizobia inoculation with integrated nutrient management are the key factors that enhance BNF [47]. Water management and planting geometry are optimized through stage-specific irrigation, water-saving designs, and crop-specific sowing densities [71]. Crop rotations and intercropping with cereals improve land-use efficiency, yield stability, and pest suppression, although they may reduce the legume's standalone yield [72]. Integrated pest management relies on cultural and biological methods, with targeted chemical control when necessary. The selection of climate-adapted, stress-tolerant, and high nitrogen-fixing varieties, supported by seed enhancements and conservation practices, underpins sustainable legume production under climate variability [73].

6. Research and development priorities

Strategic R&D investments across genomic invention, climate-resilient breeding, seed system strengthening, and postharvest value addition are destined to drive the future of legume productivity, resilience, and market competitiveness. Genomic and biotechnological advances, as well as pangenomics, are likely to play a central role in the improvement of legume cultivars [55]. High-resolution genotyping, transcriptomics, and gene-editing tools (such as CRISPR/Cas9-based systems) are now employed for accurate identification and manipulation of traits governing stress tolerance, nitrogen fixation efficiency, seed quality, and resistance to major pathogens. Unexplored diversity in wild relatives and landraces, using multiomics data integration and machine-learning-driven predictive breeding, is being utilized by researchers to resolve complex quantitative traits and exploit genetic potential [74]. The development of more vigorous and adaptable genotypes can now be accelerated. A R&D blueprint for breeding climate resilience and enhanced nutritional quality has now been established. Drought avoidance mechanisms, heat tolerance, water-use efficiency, and resistance to emerging biotic stresses in the wake of increasing temperatures, erratic rainfall, and expanding pest/disease ranges should be prioritized in breeding programs [75]. More resource investments should be channeled toward the improvement of the nutritional profiles, protein density, essential amino acids, micronutrients, and antinutritional factors of these crops. Enhanced resilience and nutritional value of these crops can be achieved through genomic selection and speed-breeding platforms without compromising yield.

Strengthening seed systems and farmer networks is eqaually important. To be impactful for farmers, improved varieties require reliable access, local adaptation, and farmer-centered dissemination pathways [76]. Early-generation seed production, promoting quality-assured community seed schemes, and supporting small and medium-scale seed enterprises should be encouraged [77]. Seed adoption may be enhanced by aligning breeding outputs with local preferences, allowing farmers to participate in the selection of cultivars/varieties, farmer-led trials, and digital advisory tools. Extension systems should be strengthened, and multistakeholder innovation platforms established to ensure feedback loops between researchers, seed producers, and farmers [78].

There exist many opportunities for value addition and improvement in the postharvest management of leguminous crops. Further research and studies are required, especially in postharvest deterioration, hermetic systems, and pest management. Improvement of processing techniques, such as, extrusion, fermentation, protein isolation, and the development of plant-based products, will create new markets to boost the competitiveness of legumes. Reduction of food waste and spoilage requires careful assessment of food quality, packaging innovations, and better logistics. At the same time, this will improve and address the burdens of modern retailers and processors. To fully realize the agronomic, nutritional, and economic potential of legumes, we must leverage these R&D priorities in genomics, climate-smart breeding, seed system development, and value chain upgrading.

7. Future prospects and policy directions in legume production

Feeding an ever-increasing population and the adoption of sustainable farming systems are the major drivers of legume production. Legumes offer a unique chance for sustainable intensification, particularly in the face of climate change pressures, soil degradation, and rising fertilizer costs [36]. Their natural ability to fix atmospheric nitrogen, compatibility with intercropping and crop rotation, and low input requirements make them key crops for achieving these goals. They maintain and boost productivity while ensuring that farming has a lower environmental impact. Systems should be put in place to grant farmers access to quality seeds and inoculants and to provide incentive-based practices that improve soil health [79]. Policies that support adaptable legume-based farming should be enacted. This will have the net effect of maximizing the ecological and agricultural benefits of legumes across diverse farming environments.

Many UN Sustainable Development Goals (SDGs) support the cultivation and production of legumes. These crops can be the powerful tools for achieving global development objectives. Legumes can help address SDG2 on Zero Hunger by providing inexpensive plant-based protein [25], and income opportunities from expanded value chains contribute to SDG1 on poverty reduction. SDG13 on Climate Action is supported by their role in improving soil fertility and reducing reliance on synthetic fertilizers [80]. Studies have shown that they can lower greenhouse gas emissions and promote resilience in smallholder farming systems. SDG15 on Life on Land is advanced through sustainable legume cultivation, which supports biodiversity and reduces chemical inputs [81]. Reinforcement of relationships among national and international agricultural policies, climate-smart agriculture, and nutrition-sensitive approaches can be supported by the wider development roadmap for legumes.

The adoption of sustainable global legume systems is the basis of food security and trade outlook. The rising population growth, health considerations, and sustainability concerns are driving the market for plant-based proteins [82]. Investments by many countries, particularly in Africa and South Asia, in the improvement of legume varieties, farmer training, and local processing and storage infrastructure have the potential to promote self-sufficiency [3]. The demand for high-quality edible beans, lentils, chickpeas, and specialty pulses is on the rise; consequently, the global trade in pulses is expected to expand significantly. Targeted policy support is therefore essential to strengthen quality standards, improve postharvest handling, and enhance phytosanitary regulations [83]. Enhancing competitiveness and enabling countries to capture greater value in domestic and international markets requires investments in value addition through cleaning, grading, packaging, and processing.

Assimilating research, institutional support, and market development in a synchronized and sequential manner is a prerequisite for establishing a strategic roadmap for the future of global legume systems. Strengthening seed systems, supporting community seed enterprises, and scaling extension services to disseminate improved agronomic practices are necessary in the interim. Focus should be placed on increasing processing capacity, enhancing storage and logistics, and integrating digital tools to help farmers access advisory services, markets, and weather information in the medium term. Moving forward, there is an urgent need to incorporate legumes into national climate strategies, agricultural investment plans, and social protection programs. To support evidence-based policy adjustments and influence, effective monitoring structures that track changes in productivity, soil health, nutrition outcomes, and environmental indicators must be put in place (**Figure 4**).

Integration of scientific innovation, rising global demand, and increasing recognition of the ecological and nutritional importance hold promise for the future of legume production. Legumes can play a transformative role in shaping resilient,

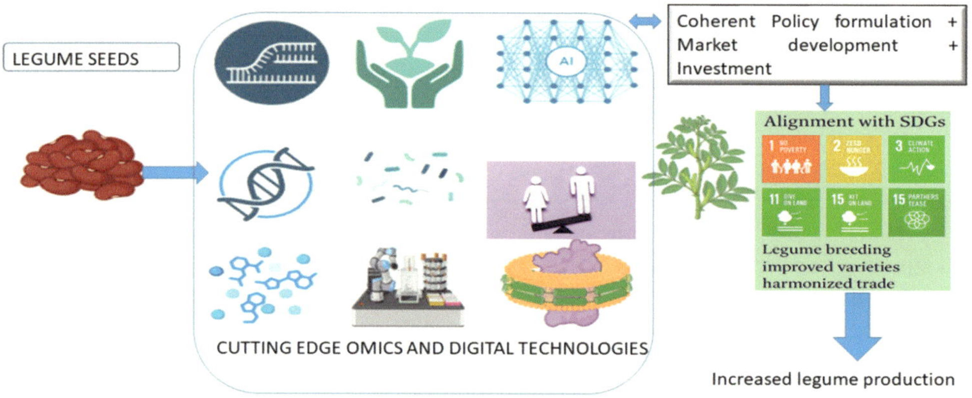

Figure 4.
Integrated approach and strategic roadmap to bridge the gap between real and potential yields.

equitable, and climate-smart food systems worldwide through coherent policies, targeted investments, and inclusive market development.

8. Conclusion

Food security, soil health, and climate resilience are heavily dependent on global legume production systems. Persistent abiotic and biotic stresses exacerbated by climate change, weak seed systems, limited markets, inadequate policy support, and structural challenges constrain production. To overcome these limitations, recent advances in genomics, precision breeding, microbial and nanobiotechnology, and digital agriculture offer solutions. Productivity, nutritional quality, and climate adaptability of legumes can be improved by embracing these technologies.
A sustainable and resilient legume sector requires coordinated investments in research, seed system strengthening, gender-responsive and farmer-centered extension. Aligning national sustainability goals, regional trade strategies, and global climate commitments will provide a clear pathway for leveraging legumes as key drivers of resilient and environmentally sound agrarian systems.

Author details

Aggrey Keya Osogo
Kibabii University, Bungoma, Kenya

*Address all correspondence to: aosogokeya@yahoo.co.uk

References

[1] Bhatti MHT, Sami A, Haider MZ, Shafiq M, Naeem S, Tariq MR, et al. Genetic diversity of vegetable crops and utilization in food and nutritional security. In: Sustainable Utilization and Conservation of Plant Genetic Diversity. Singapore: Springer Nature; 2024. p. 171–197. DOI: 10.1007/978-981-99-5245-8_6

[2] Osuna-Caballero S, Rispail N, Barilli E, Rubiales D. Management and breeding for rust resistance in legumes. Journal of Plant Pathology. 2024;1–27

[3] Breen C, Ndlovu N, McKeown PC, Spillane C. Legume seed system performance in Sub-Saharan Africa: Barriers, opportunities, and scaling options. A review. Agronomy for Sustainable Development. 2024;**44**(2):20

[4] Zhou X, Zhu T, Zhu LS, Luo SS, Deng XG, Hui LH, et al. The role of photoreceptors in response to Cucumber Mosaic Virus in Arabidopsis thaliana. Journal of Plant Growth Regulation. 2017;**36**:257–270

[5] Khan MN, Wahab S, Wahid N, Shah SN, Ullah B, Kaplan A, et al. Impact of climate change on yield and quality of legumes. Challenges and Solutions of Climate Impact on Agriculture. Elsevier. 2025;85–111. DOI: 10.1016/B978-0-443-23707-2.00004-0

[6] Meshram P. Plant Breeding for Resistance to Pests and Diseases. Bhopal, Madhya Pradesh, India: Academic Guru Publishing House; 2025

[7] Popat G, Pandey K, Sidhu GS. High-Throughput sequencing for climate resilient agriculture: Integrative genomic. Innovations in Climate Resilient Agriculture. 2025;**165**

[8] Liang X, Yu S, Ju Y, Wang Y, Yin D. Integrated management practices foster soil health, productivity, and agroecosystem resilience. Agronomy. 2025;**15**(8):1816

[9] Boukid F. Holistic benefits of plant-based foods for sustainable agrifood systems. Current Opinion in Food Science. 2024;**58**:101184

[10] Talla VVR, Sandal SS, Walia P, Vidya AS. Quality enhancement in forage crops of cereals and legumes. International Journal of Plant Soil Science. 2023;**35**(16):166–179

[11] Melese M, Getachew B, Woldemeskel E, Gunnabo AH. Legume integration in smallholder farming systems for food security and resilience to climate change. PloS One. 2025;**20**(8):e0327727

[12] Zou Y, Liu Z, Chen Y, Wang Y, Feng S. Crop rotation and diversification in China: Enhancing sustainable agriculture and resilience. Agriculture. 2024;**14**(9):1465

[13] Borazon EQ, Perera S, Alokpaï N, Venance MS, Reeve E, Harris J, et al. Policy landscape analysis for fruits and vegetables in four low-and middle-income countries through a food systems approach. PLoS One. 2025;**20**:e0331287

[14] faostat database. Google Search [Internet]. 2025. Available from: https://www.google.com/search?q=faostat+database+2025&client=firefox-b- [Accessed: 2026-January-22]

[15] Sharma A, Kaur R, Sharma V, Singh J, Popat G, Pandey K, et al. High-

throughput sequencing for climate resilient agriculture: Integrative genomic strategies and modern breeding technologies. In: Innovations in Climate Resilient Agriculture. Switzerland: Springer Nature Switzerland; 2025. p. 165–188

[16] Barbieri P, Starck T, Voisin AS, Nesme T. Biological nitrogen fixation of legumes crops under organic farming as driven by cropping management: A review. Agricultural Systems. 2023;**205**: 103579

[17] Dave K, Kumar A, Dave N, Jain M, Dhanda PS, Yadav A, et al. Climate change impacts on legume physiology and ecosystem dynamics: A multifaceted perspective. Sustainability. 2024;**16**:6026

[18] Kakwera MN, Kambewa D, Haug R. Equitable food systems in practice? The case of smallholders' marketing of legumes in Malawi. Frontiers in Sustainable Food Systems. 2025;**9**

[19] Vernooy R, Adokorach J, Kimani D, Marwa A, Mayoyo A, Nyadanu D Policies, laws, and regulations in support of farmer-managed seed systems: Still a long way to go. A review of 14 countries in Africa. 2023

[20] Michalis E, Ragkos A, Malesios C. Market-based or policy strategies to increase the cultivation of legumes for livestock? Effects on the cropping pattern and economic performance. Agricultural and Food Economics. 2025;**13**(1):3

[21] van Loon MP, Alimagham S, Pronk A, Fodor N, Ion V, Kryvoshein O, et al. Grain legume production in Europe for food, feed and meat-substitution. Global Food Security. 2023;**39**:100723

[22] Ditzler L, van Apeldoorn DF, Pellegrini F, Antichi D, Bàrberi P, Rossing WA. Current research on the ecosystem service potential of legume inclusive cropping systems in Europe. A review. Agronomy for Sustainable Development. 2021;**41**(2):26

[23] Ahmed HGMD, Naeem M, Faisal A, Fatima N, Tariq S, Owais M. Enriching the content of proteins and essential amino acids in legumes. In: Legumes Biofortification. Cham, Switzerland: Springer; 2023. p. 417–447

[24] Kunlere AS, Peter OE. Novel solutions for combating nutritional deficiencies in a crisis of growing global food insecurity

[25] Medendorp J, DeYoung D, Thiagarajan DG, Duckworth R, Pittendrigh B. A systems perspective of the role of dry beans and pulses in the future of global food security: Opportunities and challenges. Dry Beans and Pulses: Production, Processing, and Nutrition. 2022;531–550. DOI: 10.1002/9781119776802.ch21

[26] Vilakazi B, Mafongoya PL, Odindo AO, Phophi MM. The role of neglected grain legumes in food and nutrition security and human health. Sustainability. 2025;**17**(1):350

[27] Mudare S, Jing J, Makowski D, He X, Liang Z, Sims Z, et al. Crop rotations synergize yield, nutrition, and revenue: A meta-analysis. Nature Communications. 2025;**16**:9552

[28] Belachew KY, Maina NH, Dersseh WM, Zeleke B, Stoddard FL. Yield gaps of major cereal and grain

legume crops in Ethiopia: A review. Agronomy. 2022;**12**(10):2528

[29] Hazra KK, Basu PS. Pulses. In: Trajectory of 75 Years of Indian Agriculture after Independence. Singapore: Springer Nature Singapore; 2023. p. 189–230

[30] Lundqvist J, Malmquist L, Dias P, Barron J, Wakeyo MB. Water Productivity, the Yield Gap, and Nutrition: The Case of Ethiopia. Rome, Italy: Food & Agriculture Org; 2021

[31] Islam MS, Fahad S, Hossain A, Chowdhury MK, Iqbal MA, Dubey A, et al. Legumes under drought stress: Plant responses, adaptive mechanisms, and management strategies in relation to nitrogen fixation. In: Engineering tolerance in crop plants against abiotic stress. [Internet]. CRC Press; 2021. p. 179–207. Available from: https://api.taylorfrancis.com/content/chapters/edit/download?identifierName=doi&identifierValue=10.1201/9781003160717-9&type=chapterpdf [Accessed: 2025-November-22]

[32] Tawaha ARM, Alatrash H, Jabbour Y, Al-Tawaha AR, Qaisi AM, Jammal R, et al. Drought Stress and Sustainable Legume Production. In: Marker-Assisted Breeding in Legumes for Drought Tolerance. Singapore: Springer Nature Singapore; 2025. p. 23–40

[33] Raja MM, Vijayalakshmi G, Naik ML, Basha PO, Sergeant K, Hausman JF, et al. Pollen development and function under heat stress: From effects to responses. Acta Physiologiae Plantarum. 2019;**41**:47

[34] Xu R, Pu Z, Han S, Yu H, Guo C, Huang Q, et al. Managing forage for grain: Strategies and mechanisms for enhancing forage production to ensure feed grain security. Journal of Integrative Agriculture. 2025;**24**(6):1

[35] Renaudeau D, Jensen SK, Ambye-Jensen M, Adler S, Bani P, Juncker E, et al. Nutritional values of forage-legume-based silages and protein concentrates for growing pigs. animal. 2022;**16**(7):100572

[36] Dubeux Jr JC, Jaramillo DM, Santos ER, Garcia L, Queiroz LM, Bretas IL, et al. Sustainable intensification of livestock systems using forage legumes in the Anthropocene. Grass and Forage Science. 2024;**79**:481–498

[37] Notz I, Topp CF, Schuler J, Alves S, Gallardo LA, Dauber J, et al. Transition to legume-supported farming in Europe through redesigning cropping systems. Agronomy for Sustainable Development. 2023;**43**:12

[38] Bhatla SC, Kathpalia R. Essential and functional mineral elements. In: Plant Physiology, Development and Metabolism. Singapore: Springer Nature Singapore; 2023. p. 25–49

[39] Jena J, Maitra S, Hossain A, Pramanick B, Gitari HI, Praharaj S, et al. Role of legumes in cropping system for soil ecosystem improvement. Ecosystem Services: Types, Management and Benefits Nova Science Publishers, Inc. 2022;**415**:1–21

[40] Mehmood M, Tanveer NA, Joyia FA, Ullah I, Mohamed HI. Effect of high temperature on pollen grains and yield in economically important crops: A review. Planta. 2025;**261**(6):141

[41] Dixit GP, Srivastava AK, Jayalakshmi V, Bindra S, Singh S. Chickpea breeding. In Fundamentals of

Field Crop Breeding. Singapore: Springer Nature Singapore; 2022. p. 1009–1062

[42] Pandey K, Saharan BS. Soil microbiomes: A promising strategy for boosting crop yield and advancing sustainable agriculture. Discover Agriculture. 2025;**3**(1):54

[43] Jalal A, Filho MCMT, da Silva EC, da Silva Oliveira CE, Freitas LA, Do Nascimento V. Plant growth-promoting bacteria and nitrogen fixing bacteria: Sustainability of non-legume crops. In: Nitrogen Fixing Bacteria: Sustainable Growth of Non-legumes. Singapore: Springer Nature Singapore; 2022. p. 233–275

[44] Surendran U, Nagakumar KCV, Samuel MP. Remote Sensing in Precision Agriculture. In: Digital Agriculture: A Solution for Sustainable Food and Nutritional Security. Cham: Springer International Publishing, Switzerland; 2024. p. 201–223

[45] Meena BR, Biswas KK. Status of the major aphid-transmitted viruses of pulse crops in India. Indian Phytopathology. 2024;**77**(3):561–572

[46] Mandumbu R, Mutengwa C, Mabasa S, Mwenje E. Challenges to the exploitation of host plant resistance for Striga management in cereals and legumes by farmers in sub-Saharan Africa: A review. Acta Agriculturae Scandinavica, Section B—Soil & Plant Science. 2019;**69**(1):82–88

[47] Khan MN, Ijaz M, Ali Q, Ul-Allah S, Sattar A, Ahmad S. Biological nitrogen fixation in nutrient management. In: Agronomic Crops: Volume 2: Management Practices. Singapore: Springer Singapore; 2019. p. 127–147

[48] Mendoza-Suárez M, Andersen SU, Poole PS, Sánchez-Cañizares C. Competition, nodule occupancy, and persistence of inoculant strains: Key factors in the rhizobium-legume symbioses. Frontiers in Plant Science. 2021;**12**:690567

[49] Skendžić S, Zovko M, Živković IP, Lešić V, Lemić D.The impact of climate change on agricultural insect pests. Insects. 2021;**12**(5):440

[50] Resentini F, Orozco-Arroyo G, Cucinotta M, Mendes MA. The impact of heat stress in plant reproduction. Frontiers in Plant Science. 2023;**14**:1271644

[51] Nega A. Climate change impacts on agriculture: A review of plant diseases and insect pests in Ethiopia and East Africa, with adaptation and mitigation strategies. Advances in Agriculture. 2025;**2025**(1):5606701

[52] Ambika AMS, Gayacharan HA, Talukdar A, Kumar Gupta S, et al. Unraveling origin, history, genetics, and strategies for accelerated domestication and diversification of food legumes. Frontiers in Genetics. 2022;**13**:932430

[53] Shukla S, Tripathi A, Joshi T, Sharma A, Shukla SK. Molecular Markers and Marker-Assisted Breeding in Pulses. In: Molecular Markers and Crop Improvement: Principle and Application. Cham: Springer Nature Switzerland; 2025. p. 125–142

[54] Jha UC, Nayyar H, Parida SK, Bakır M, von Wettberg EJ, Siddique KH. Progress of genomics-driven approaches for sustaining underutilized legume crops in the post-genomic era. Frontiers in Genetics. 2022;**13**:831656

[55] Hu H, Yuan X, Saini DK, Yang T, Wu X, Wu R, et al. A panomics-driven framework for the improvement of major food legume crops: Advances, challenges, and future prospects. Horticulture Research. 2025;**12**(7): uhaf091

[56] Ullah A, Farooq M. The challenge of drought stress for grain legumes and options for improvement. Archives of Agronomy and Soil Science. 2022;**68** (11):1601–1618

[57] Singh G, Gudi S, Amandeep Upadhyay P, Shekhawat PK, Nayak G, et al. Unlocking the hidden variation from wild repository for accelerating genetic gain in legumes. Frontiers in Plant Science. 2022;**13**:1035878

[58] Chaudhary D, Pal N, Arora A, Prashant BD, Venadan S. Plant functional traits in crop breeding: Advancement and challenges. In: Plant Functional Traits for Improving Productivity. Singapore: Springer Nature Singapore; 2024. p. 169–202

[59] Kashem MA, Hossain MZ. Climate-induced droughts and its implications for legume crops. In: Climate Change and Legumes. Boca Raton, FL, USA: CRC Press; 2023. p. 189–206

[60] Alioma R, Zeller M, Ling YK. Analysis of long-term prices of micronutrient-dense and starchy staple foods in developing countries. Agricultural and Food Economics. 2022;**10**(1):24

[61] Marjit S, Mishra S. Credit market imperfection, lack of entrepreneurship and capital outflow from a developing economy. Review of Development Economics. 2023;**27**(3):1855–1873

[62] Alemayehu D, Dechassa N. Inoculating faba bean seed with rhizobium bacteria increases the yield of the crop and saves farmers from the cost of applying phosphorus fertilizer. International Journal of Plant Production. 2022;**16**(2):261–273

[63] Akram-Lodhi AH ' Trapped Inside a World of Labor': Gender Gaps in Agricultural Productivity and Reproductive Labor in Malawi. 2025

[64] Boehm J. The impact of contract enforcement costs on value chains and aggregate productivity. Review of Economics and Statistics. 2022;**104** (1):34–50

[65] Saxena KB, Saxena RK. Pigeonpea [Cajanus cajan (L.) Millsp.] Breeding. In: Fundamentals of Legume Breeding: A Text for Students and Practitioners. Singapore: Springer Nature Singapore; 2025. p. 51–75

[66] Kumar R, Das SP, Choudhury BU, Kumar A, Prakash NR, Verma R, et al. Advances in genomic tools for plant breeding: Harnessing DNA molecular markers, genomic selection, and genome editing. Biological Research. 2024;**57**:80

[67] Dasgupta U, Bharath S, Dutta S. Abiotic Stress and Legume Production. In: Marker-Assisted Breeding in Legumes for Drought Tolerance. Singapore: Springer Nature Singapore; 2025. p. 1–21

[68] Ahmed T, Noman M, Qi Y, Shahid M, Hussain S, Masood HA, et al. Fertilization of microbial composts: A technology for improving stress resilience in plants. Plants. 2023;**12**:3550

[69] Singh NK, Sunitha NH, Tripathi G, Saikanth DRK, Sharma A, Jose AE, et al.

Impact of digital technologies in agricultural extension. Asian Journal of Agricultural Extension, Economics & Sociology. 2023;**41**:963–970

[70] Tahir MA, Hamza A, Hussain S, Xie Z, Brestic M, Rastogi A, et al. Carbon sequestrating fertilizers as a tool for carbon sequestration in agriculture under aridisols. Carbon Letters. 2022;**32**:1631–1644

[71] Dakhore KK, Kadam YE, Kadam DR, Jadhav AS, Ghosh K, Bal SK, et al. Stage-Specific Crop Coefficients for Cotton in Central India: A Comprehensive Analysis. Journal of Agronomy and Crop Science. 2025;**211**: e70098

[72] Raza MA, Zhiqi W, Yasin HS, Gul H, Qin R, Rehman SU, et al. Effect of crop combination on yield performance, nutrient uptake, and land use advantage of cereal/legume intercropping systems. Field Crops Research. 2023;**304**:109144

[73] Abdallah NA, Hamwieh A, Radwan K, Fouad N, Baum M. Climate-smart Crops: Delivering Tolerant Genes Based on Engineered Nanocarriers and CRISPR/Cas Genome-editing System. Stress-Resilient Crops: Coordinated omics-CRISPR-nanotechnology Strategies. GB: CABI. 2025;511–539

[74] Nikitha J, Alagu M. Post-genomic Era in Crop Breeding. In: Plant Breeding 2050: Next-Gen Crops. Singapore: Springer Nature Singapore; 2025. p. 317–358

[75] Hossain MZ, Anawar HM, Chaudhary DR. Climate Change and Legumes: Stress Mitigation for Sustainability and Food Security. USA: CRC Press; 2023

[76] Prajapati CS, Priya NK, Bishnoi S, Vishwakarma SK, Buvaneswari K, Shastri S, et al. The role of participatory approaches in modern agricultural extension: Bridging knowledge gaps for sustainable farming practices. Journal of Experimental Agriculture International. 2025;**47**:204–222

[77] Hein I, Bayer M, Chen X, Hunter-Brown L, Wang Y, Kaur A, et al. Tracking the deployment of functional disease resistance genes in cultivars to inform breeding. 2022

[78] Chinseu EL, Dougill AJ, Stringer LC. Strengthening Conservation Agriculture innovation systems in sub-Saharan Africa: Lessons from a stakeholder analysis. International Journal of Agricultural Sustainability. 2022;**20**(1):17–30

[79] Shahid N. Legumes Production Under Changing Climate. In: Climate Smart Agriculture for Future Food Security. Singapore: Springer Nature Singapore; 2025. p. 191–221

[80] Owusu-Sekyere E, Nyam YS, Selelo OT, Torsu DA. Sustainable Development Goal 13: Urgent action to combat climate change and its impacts. In: Handbook on Public Policy and Food Security. Cheltenham, UK: Edward Elgar Publishing; 2024. p. 311–321

[81] Fitawek W, Hendriks SL. Sustainable Development Goal 15: Life on land. In: Handbook on Public Policy and Food Security. Cheltenham, UK: Edward Elgar Publishing; 2024. p. 354–364

[82] Sharma N, Yeasmen N, Dube L, Orsat V. Rise of plant-based beverages: A consumer-driven perspective. Food Reviews International. 2024;**40**(10):3315–3341

[83] Osei-Kwarteng M, Ogwu MC, Mahunu GK, Afoakwah NA. Post-harvest Food Quality and Safety in the Global South: Sustainable Management Perspectives. In: Food Safety and Quality in the Global South. Singapore: Springer Nature Singapore; 2024. p. 151–195

Chapter 5

Neglected and Underutilized Legume Crops: Key Insights into Origin, Botany, Benefits, Constraints and Recent Research Focus

Naser A. Anjum, Asim Masood, Iqra Khan, Abdul Enam, Tehreem Fatima, Rizah Akbar, Palaniswamy Thangavel, Alexander S. Lukatkin, Shahid Umar and Nafees A. Khan

Abstract

The requirement for proteins in the balanced human diet is fulfilled by both plant and animal sources. In particular, plant-based proteins are lower in saturated fat, high in fibre, and contribute roughly 32%–65% of the global supply. Among the plant-based protein sources, legume crops (family Fabaceae/Leguminosae; seeds are produced in pods) are widely known to sustainably provide roughly 20%–45% protein content (about twice that of cereals). Hence, legumes are key to meeting human dietary needs, particularly in vegetarian diets. Notably, traditional and commonly cultivated legumes (e.g., soybean, *Glycine max*; chickpea, *Cicer arietinum*; common bean, *Phaseolus vulgaris*; and pigeon pea, *Cajanus cajan*) dominate the plant-based protein market. Despite possessing comparable or superior nutritional profiles, higher protein content, and enhanced climate resilience, most underutilized and neglected legumes (e.g., Bambara groundnut, *Vigna subterranea*; winged bean, *Psophocarpus tetragonolobus*; and horse gram, *Macrotyloma uniflorum*) have been largely overlooked by mainstream agricultural research, policy, and global markets in favour of high-yielding staples. Taking into account the selected neglected and underutilized legume crops, this chapter aims to: (1) provide an overview of key insights into their origin and botany, (2) highlight the major constraints responsible for the neglect of these legume crops, (3) briefly illuminate important areas of recent research on these leguminous crop types, and (4) list aspects that have so far been overlooked or least explored in this context. Future research in this direction may be devised by utilizing the major outcomes of the discussion.

Keywords: balanced diet, protein, legume, underutilized legume crops, legume crops origin, legume crop botany

 IntechOpen

1. Introduction

Human health maintenance and functions require a balanced diet, which consists of six essential nutrient groups – carbohydrates, proteins, fats, vitamins, minerals, and water (often including fibre; see **Figure 1**). Apart from providing essential nutrients for energy, strong immunity, and proper body functions, a balanced diet significantly lowers the risk of chronic diseases like heart disease, diabetes, and certain cancers, and also supports mental well-being, healthy weight management, and better sleep [1, 2].

Among the six essential nutrient groups in a balanced human diet, proteins are crucial for tissue growth, repair, and muscle maintenance in humans. Both plant and animal sources significantly fulfill the protein requirement in a balanced human diet and provide essential amino acids necessary for maintaining health, growth, and development. Generally considered 'complete' (containing all nine essential amino acids), animal proteins (sourced mainly from meat, dairy, fish, and eggs) are highly bioavailable, efficient for muscle protein synthesis, and have higher digestibility. On the contrary, plant proteins (sourced mainly from soybean, *Glycine max*; chickpea, *Cicer arietinum*; common bean, *Phaseolus vulgaris*; and pigeon pea, *Cajanus cajan*) are also excellent, sustainable options that are typically richer in fibre and phytonutrients [3, 4]. Increasingly recognized as superior to animal-based proteins, plant-based proteins significantly contribute to human health and environmental sustainability. To this end, plant-based sources (versus animal protein) significantly reduce the risk of chronic diseases, including heart disease, type 2 diabetes, and certain cancers. Additionally, plant-based proteins also offer a much smaller environmental footprint, requiring less land and water, and emitting fewer greenhouse gases compared to animal proteins [5] (see **Figure 2**).

Among the plant-based protein sources, legumes (plants in the pea family Fabaceae or Leguminosae) are essential, cost-effective plant-based protein sources (typically 20%–45% dry weight) and significantly meet global food

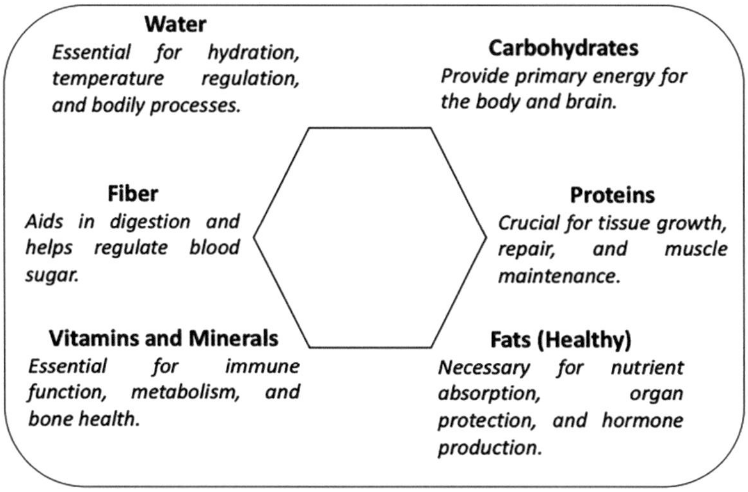

Figure 1.
Representation of key components (and their important functions) in a balanced human diet.

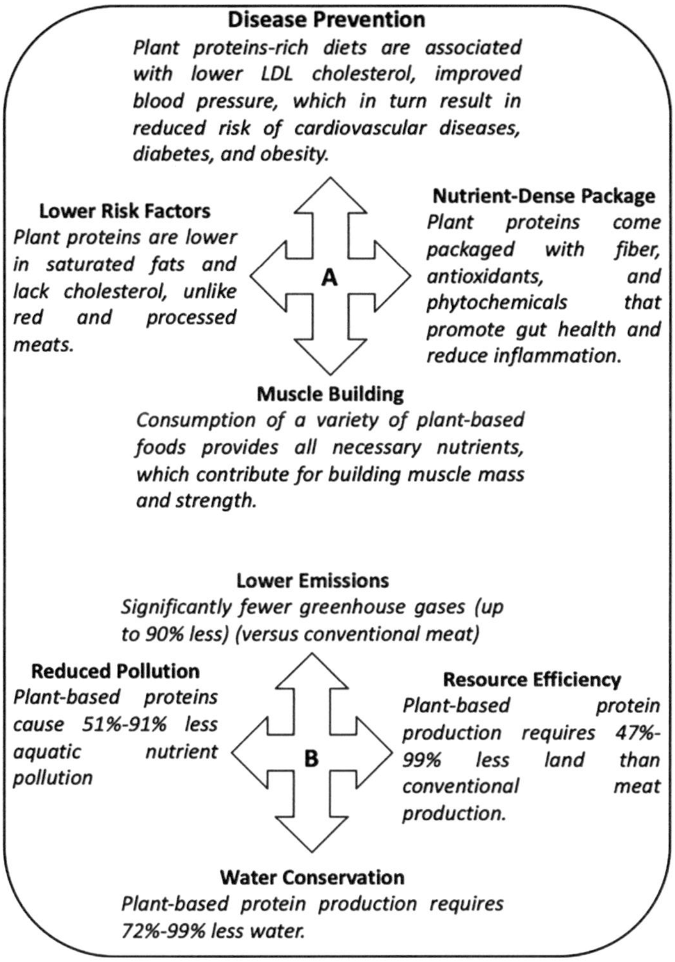

Figure 2.
Representation of the major contributions of plant-based proteins to (a) the health of humans and (b) the environment.

protein requirements (particularly in vegetarian diets) [6–8]. Major legume crops (traditional legume crops) are widely cultivated, have well-established supply chains, and enjoy high consumer awareness. The list of these major (traditional) legume crops includes *Glycine max* (gold standard, a complete protein source; with 36%–44% protein and 19%–20% oil); *Cicer arietinum* (17%–22% protein and high in fibre and minerals); *Phaseolus vulgaris* (16%–25% protein); and *Cajanus cajan* (19%–21.7% protein and vital in tropical diets). There are other legume crops that are mostly underutilized and neglected (underutilized and neglected legume crops). Although more nutrient-dense and climate-resilient, underutilized and neglected legume crops are under-researched and under-marketed. The list of underutilized and neglected legume crops includes winged bean (*Psophocarpus tetragonolobus*; 32%–37% protein; edible parts include seeds, leaves, flowers, and tubers); Bambara groundnut (*Vigna subterranea*; 18%–24% protein; notable for drought tolerance and high nutritional value); horse gram

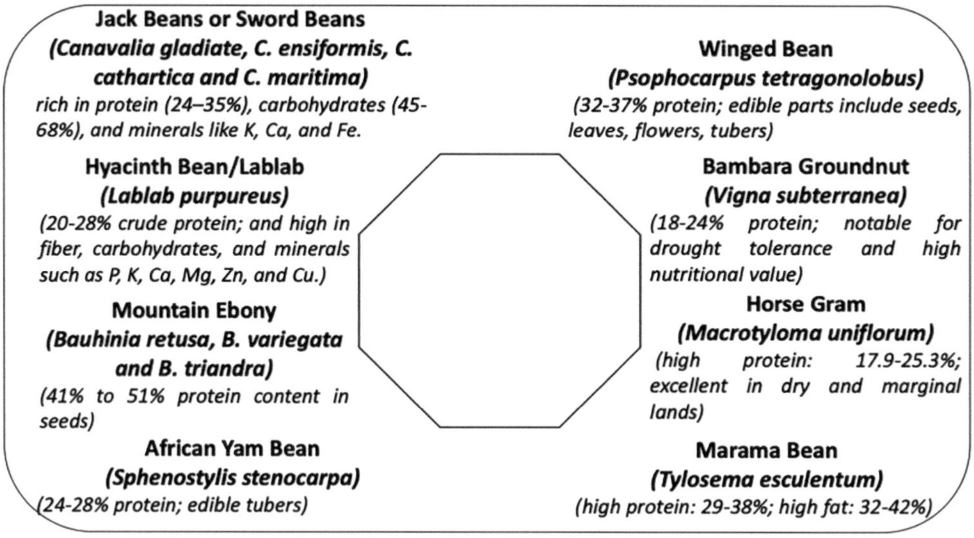

Figure 3.
Representation of important underutilized and neglected legume crops.

(*Macrotyloma uniflorum*; high protein: 17.9%–25.3%; excellent in dry and marginal lands); Marama bean (*Tylosema esculentum*; high protein: 29%–38%; high fat: 32%–42%); African yam bean (*Sphenostylis stenocarpa*; 24%–28% protein; edible tubers); mountain ebony (*Bauhinia retusa*, *B. variegata,* and *B. triandra*; 41% to 51% protein content in seeds); and Jack beans or Sword beans (*Canavalia gladiata*, *C. ensiformis*, *C. cathartica,* and *C. maritima*; protein content 30%–36%; see **Figure 3**). Interestingly, most neglected and underutilized legume crops (versus traditional legume crops) are unique in terms of nutritional superiority, climate change resilience, and functional uses. To this end, some underutilized legumes like *Bauhinia* sp. and *Canavalia* sp. have higher protein content (>40%) than *G. max*. Underutilized legumes are often more resistant to extreme conditions (e.g., drought, salinity, and heat) due to their hardiness, making them vital for future food security. Moreover, underutilized legumes often have better digestibility of starch and provide unique functional properties, such as high water/oil absorption for food manufacturing. Overall, underutilized legumes can be considered 'future smart foods' that may offer a solution to both malnutrition and climate change, provide a high-protein, sustainable alternative to mainstream crops and animal protein, and eventually contribute to food, nutritional, and environmental security, which are the crying need of the time on the globe [8–12].

Given above, taking into account the selected neglected and underutilized legume crops, this chapter: (1) overviews key insights into their origin, botany, and benefits; (2) highlights the major constraints responsible for the negligence of these legume crops; (3) briefly enlightens important focuses of the recent research on these leguminous crop types; and also (4) lists, so far, overlooked or least explored aspects to this end. The outcomes of the discussion may help in devising future research in the current direction.

DOI: http://dx.doi.org/10.5772/intechopen.1015213

1.1 Origin, key botanical insights and benefits

1.1.1 Bambara groundnut

Associated with the historic Bambara Empire (one of the largest states of West Africa in the eighteenth century), Bambara groundnut (underground bean; *Vigna subterranea*) has West Africa as its primary centre of origin. *V. subterranea var. spontanea*, the wild form of *V. subterranea,* was identified in the early twentieth century in Northern Nigeria and Northern Cameroon. Formerly named *Voandzeia subterranea*, *V. subterranea* was reclassified to the genus *Vigna* (related to cowpeas) [13]. This hardy legume is predominantly cultivated by smallholder farmers in semi-arid sub-Saharan Africa and has its major production in Nigeria, Niger, Burkina Faso, and Cameroon. An annual herbaceous plant, *V. subterranea* attains a height between 0.25 and 0.37 m and grows with branched stems that form a crown, either in bunched, semi-bunched, or spreading forms. *V. subterranea* possesses a taproot system with numerous nitrogen-fixing nodules, allowing it to thrive in nutrient-poor soils. Its leaves are compound, trifoliate (three leaflets), and possess stipules (about 3 mm long). Pale-yellow, self-fertilizing (cleistogamous) flowers appear 40–60 days after planting. Fruits/pods, formed below the soil surface, are indehiscent (do not split open at maturity), wrinkled, somewhat round, and roughly 2.5 cm in diameter. Smooth, round, or unilaterally flattened and extremely hard (when dry) seeds come in various colours (e.g., white, cream, brown, red, or mottled). *V. subterranea* has been argued to be a highly nutritious, drought-tolerant, 'complete food' legume, which boasts 18%–28% protein and significant fibre. Owing to the availability of high iron, potassium, and a low glycemic index, *V. subterranea* significantly aids in managing diabetes, cardiovascular diseases, and anaemia. This climate-resilient crop also improves soil fertility [14–16].

1.1.2 African yam bean

Indigenous to Africa, the African yam bean (*Sphenostylis stenocarpa*) has Ethiopia as its centre of origin and highest genetic diversity. A tuberous legume, *S. stenocarpa* is widely cultivated as a significant food security crop for its edible aerial grains and subterranean tubers in West and Central Africa, particularly in Nigeria, Ghana, Cameroon, and Togo [17, 18]. This underutilized tropical legume grows as a climbing herbaceous vine with strong tendrils that twine on stakes. Unlike other legumes, *S. stenocarpa* also produces edible tubers. *S. stenocarpa* develops a root system with nitrogen-fixing nodules and elongated, fleshy tubers that resemble sweet potatoes. Its trifoliate leaves have ovate-lanceolate leaflets (2.7–13 cm long). Pink- to purple-coloured, self-pollinating flowers exhibit raceme inflorescence (4–10 flowers per raceme). It also possesses a dorsiventrally flattened and bearded-edge stigma. Long, linear, flat or ridged pods (20–30 cm long) turn brown and shatter at maturity. Seeds (without aril) vary in size and colour and can be white, black, brown, or mottled [19, 20]. A highly nutritious and underutilized legume, *S. stenocarpa* is packed with 25% protein (comparable to *G. max*) and roughly 75% carbohydrates. Given these attributes, and being enriched in antioxidants, fibre, minerals (e.g., Ca, Mg, and Fe), and low in glycemic index, *S. stenocarpa* offers significant health benefits, such as managing diabetes, reducing cardiovascular disease risk, and combating malnutrition [21–23].

1.1.3 Winged bean

The highest genetic diversity of the winged bean (*Psophocarpus tetragonolobus*) occurs in South-East Asia or Papua New Guinea, where this wonderful but neglected and underutilized legume crop is believed to have originated. However, due to similarities with other African *Psophocarpus* species (e.g., *Psophocarpus grandiflorus*), the origin of *P. tetragonolobus* has also been linked to Africa [24–26]. Exhibiting vigorous twining, *P. tetragonolobus* is a herbaceous perennial vine that grows 3–5 m tall (and is typically supported by trellises). This legume crop develops a robust, tuberous root system, which is edible and high in protein. Its trifoliate leaves are bright green and have ovate to deltoid-shaped leaflets (10–15 cm long).
A predominantly self-pollinated legume crop, it has large (2.5–3.5 cm wide) and papilionaceous (pea-like) flowers, which appear in clusters (racemes) and exhibit a diversity of colours (white, blue, or dark purple). Pods (fruits) are four-angled with distinct and frilled wings (running along each edge). White-, yellow-, brown-, or black-coloured seeds are spherical and smooth [26, 27]. Widely cultivated throughout the hot, humid, tropical, and sub-tropical regions of South and Southeast Asia (e.g., Thailand, Indonesia, Papua New Guinea, Bangladesh) and Africa, *P. tetragonolobus* has been a popular legume crop in Assam, Tripura, Meghalaya, West Bengal, and various southern states [24–26, 28]. Often called a 'super legume', 'One Species Supermarket', or 'Supermarket on a Stalk', *P. tetragonolobus* is a highly nutritious, versatile, and underutilized tropical legume. This legume crop has been considered a crucial crop for fighting malnutrition owing to the edible nature of nearly every part, such as its protein-rich pods, seeds, leaves, and tubers. Moreover, owing to the availability of high protein (27%–45% in seeds), fibre, vitamins A and C, and essential minerals, this 'super legume' offers significant health benefits, supports digestive health, boosts immunity, and promotes cardiovascular health [25, 28].

1.1.4 Marama bean

Arid and semi-arid regions of Southern Africa, primarily the Kalahari Desert in Botswana, Namibia (e.g., Omaheke and Otjizondjupa regions), and parts of South Africa, have been regarded as the origin of the Marama bean (*Tylosema esculentum*). *T. esculentum* has served as a traditional food source for the Khoisan and Bantu people (two distinct, major populations in Southern Africa with different ancestral, linguistic, and cultural histories). Moreover, this wild, drought-tolerant, perennial legume also has significant ethnobotanical importance and is known as the 'green gold of Africa' since it is a vital, non-domesticated source of protein (30%–39%) and oil (30%–43%) [29, 30]. *T. esculentum* is primarily wild-harvested in Botswana, Namibia, and South Africa (particularly the North West, Northern Cape, Limpopo, and Gauteng provinces) [31]. A long-lived, prostrate, herbaceous perennial, *T. esculentum* often forms mats. *T. esculentum* possesses large (up to 10 kg), deep-rooted tubers, which store water and allow the plant to thrive in arid conditions. The leaves of *T. esculentum* are succulent when young and leathery when mature, exhibiting a characteristic 'cow-hoof' or bi-lobed shape. Yellow flowers (25 mm in length) are borne in racemes. *The* pods and seeds of *T. esculentum* are woody and flattened, containing one to two large, brown–black, round-to-oval seeds [29]. *T. esculentum*, a long-lived perennial, produces tubers for water storage and possesses highly nutritious seeds (typically one to two seeds per pod) containing 30%–39% protein and 35%–48% lipid, similar to *Glycine max*. Its edible tubers, along with the availability of Fe, Zn, Ca, and antioxidants, provide several health benefits. Additionally, *T. esculentum* has traditional medicinal uses, including treating diarrhoea, inflammation, and infections [31, 32].

1.1.5 Hyacinth bean/lablab

Eastern and Southern Africa is considered the geographical origin (and also the cradle of its domestication) of the Hyacinth Bean or Lablab (*Lablab purpureus*), where significant wild-type diversity exists. However, sources also suggest Southeast Asia as the primary origin of this underutilized legume crop, where it was domesticated, dispersed, and cultivated. Notably, early cultivation (and use) of *L. purpureus* was noted in India, dating back to at least 2500 BC [33, 34]. Although cultivated in nearly all continents, wide cultivation of *L. purpureus* (for its young seeds and pods) by small-farm holders (as a versatile, low-input crop) was noted in tropical and subtropical regions (Asia and Africa). However, *L. purpureus* has its major production in India, Southeast Asia, East/West Africa, Egypt, and Sudan [35, 36]. A monotypic genus within the Fabaceae family, *L. purpureus* is a herbaceous perennial (but cultivated as an annual) and exhibits a climbing and twining vine habit. Having a strong, deep taproot system (contributing to drought resistance), its alternate and trifoliate (three leaflets) leaves possess ovate–triangular to rhombic leaflets (10–50 cm long). Typically purple or white flowers of *L. purpureus* exhibit an axillary raceme (10–60 cm long) type of inflorescence. Ranging from green to vibrant purple, flattened and curved pods/fruits (3.5–14 cm long) typically contain three to six seeds. Exhibiting colour diversity (white, brown, red, black), seeds possess a conspicuous white hilum (eye) [37, 38]. Owing to the availability of high protein (20%–28%), fibre (both soluble and insoluble), calcium (Ca), phosphorus (P), iron (Fe), potassium (K), and magnesium (Mg), the highly nutritious, drought-tolerant legume *L. purpureus* promotes heart health, weight loss, and improved digestion. It also helps manage blood sugar levels, supports strong bone health, and combats malnutrition as well [38–40].

2. Major constraints

2.1 Bambara groundnut

The production of *V. subterranea* is largely constrained by reliance on low-yielding landraces, lack of improved varieties, and, despite its resilience, susceptibility to field pests, diseases (such as leaf spot and viruses), and poor storage. On the contrary, limited research support, high labour demands for harvesting, and slow adoption of modern processing technologies can be included under the category of socio-economic challenges for *V. subterranea* [41, 42] (see **Figure 4**).

2.2 African yam bean

Long cooking times (up to 24 hours), the need for staking, a long maturation period (seven to eight months), and the presence of antinutritional factors

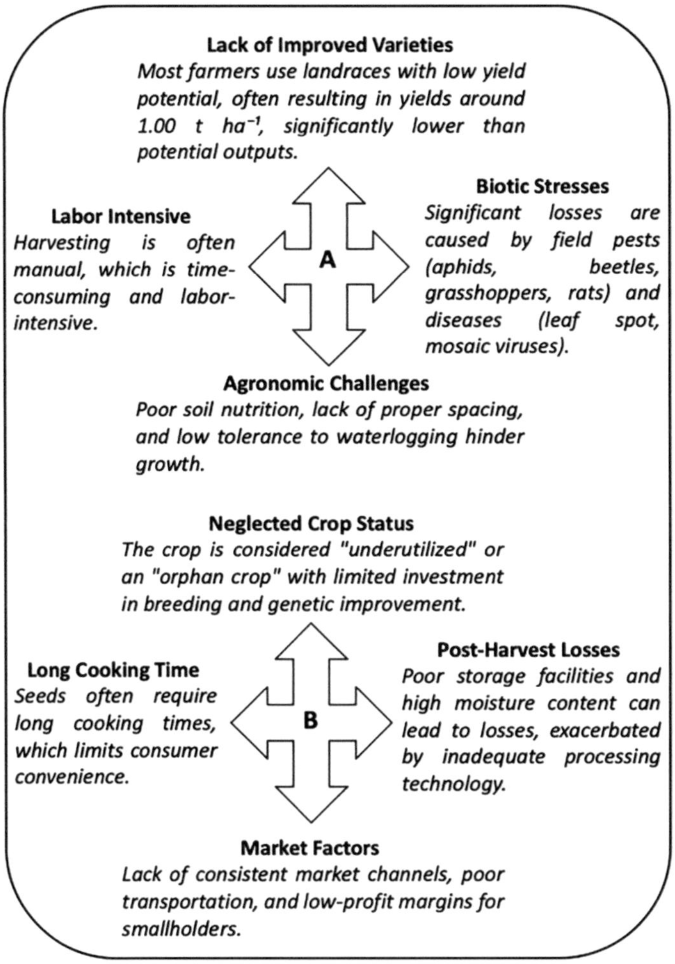

Figure 4.
Representation of (a) key agricultural and genetic constraints and (b) socio-economic and post-harvest constraints in the production of Bambara groundnut (underground bean; Vigna subterranea*).*

(e.g., trypsin inhibitors, phytates, tannins, oxalates, and lectins) are on the list of important constraints for *S. stenocarpa*. In addition, the production of this underutilized legume crop is also limited by declining interest, a high incidence of viral diseases, pest susceptibility (thrips, pod borers), and high labour demands for cultivation [22, 23].

2.3 Winged bean

The indeterminate and vigorous climbing growth habit (requiring high-labour staking), a lengthy maturation period, and high sensitivity to environmental conditions (such as frost and waterlogging) are among the major constraints in cultivating *P. tetragonolobus*. A list of other important constraints for *P. tetragonolobus* cultivation includes low seed yield, limited improved cultivars, susceptibility to root-knot nematodes, and high levels of antinutritional factors (e.g., trypsin/

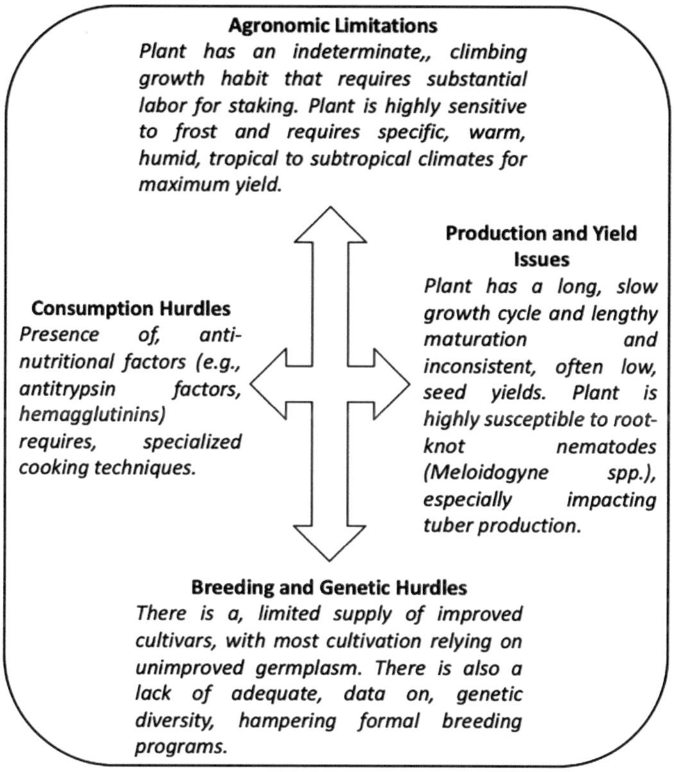

Figure 5.
*Representation of key constraints (and challenges) in the production of winged bean (*Psophocarpus tetragonolobus*).*

chymotrypsin inhibitors, phytates, lectins [hemagglutinins], tannins, and oxalates) [27, 43] (see **Figure 5**).

2.4 Marama bean

The development of *T. esculentum* is constrained by several factors, including its reliance on wild harvesting, low and inconsistent seed yields (often one to two seeds per pod), and the lack of domesticated, high-yielding cultivars. In addition, its long, slow growth cycle (flowering after two to four years), sensitivity to waterlogging, and limited seed germination (due to a hard, tough seed coat requiring specialized pretreatment) are other major constraints for *T. esculentum* [44, 45].

2.5 Hyacinth bean/lablab

The list of important constraints for *L. purpureus* includes salinity stress, anti-nutritional factors (e.g., cyanogenic glycosides, trypsin inhibitors, phytic acid, tannins, and saponins), pests, and disease susceptibility. Moreover, poor management, lack of technical knowledge, and sensitivity to waterlogging or heavy grazing are other major constraints for *L. purpureus*, a resilient, underutilized, and nutritious legume [46–48] (see **Figure 6**).

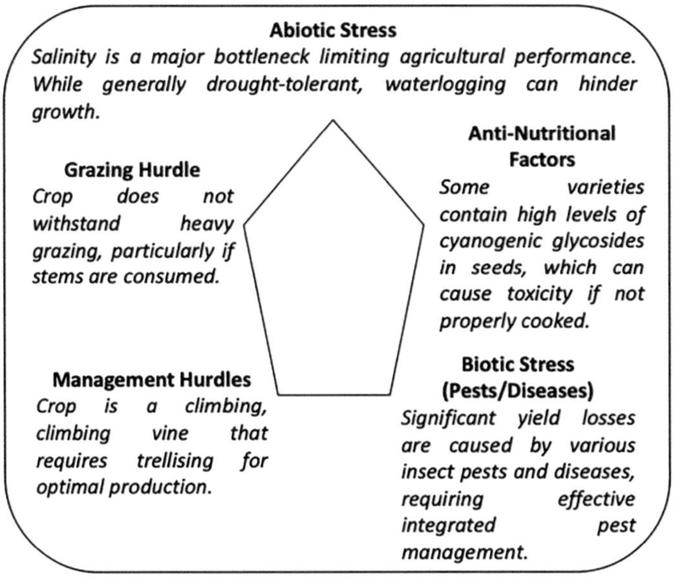

Figure 6.
*Representation of key constraints in the production of hyacinth bean (*Lablab purpureus*).*

3. Recent research focus

3.1 Bambara groundnut

Recent research on *V. subterranea* focuses on its potential as a climate-resilient, nutrient-dense 'future food' to combat malnutrition and food insecurity in arid regions. Moreover, efforts are being made to focus on its nutritional and health benefits, climate resilience and cultivation, genetic improvement and accessions, and sustainability and farming systems [42, 49–51] (see **Figure 7**).

3.2 African yam bean

Key focus areas of recent research on *S. stenocarpa* include genetic improvement and breeding (for shorter cooking times, higher yields, and enhanced resistance to diseases); nutritional and health profiling (aimed at highlighting its role as a 'nutraceutical' due to its high protein, iron, and fibre content); functional food development (aimed at using *S. stenocarpa* to fortify or enrich staples like breakfast foods and snacks to improve nutritional value); agricultural production and pest management (aimed at optimizing its nitrogen-fixing capabilities for sustainable intercropping and identifying fungal diseases); and underutilization and value chain enhancement (aimed at investigating why the crop remains underutilized compared to *G. max* or cowpea, *Vigna unguiculata*) [22, 23, 52].

3.3 Winged bean

Owing to its potential as a nutrient-dense legume crop, *P. tetragonolobus* is being researched to further exploit its potential as a 'superfood' and sustainable

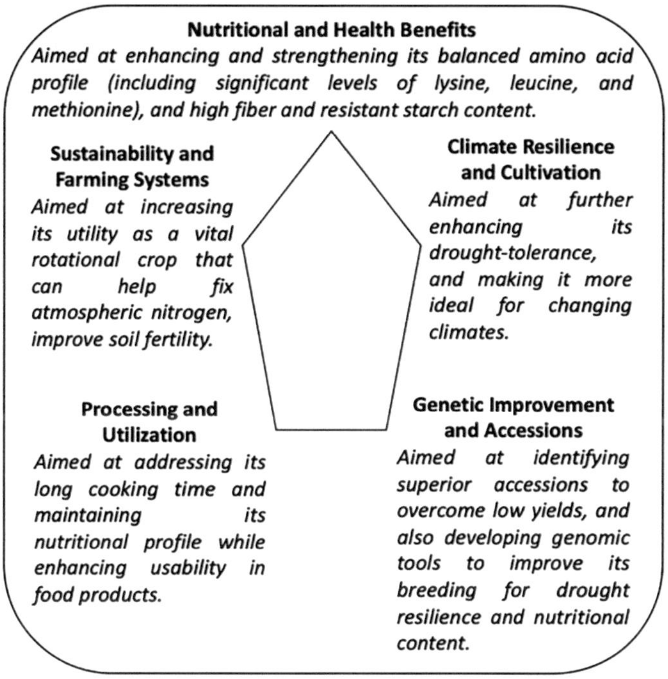

Figure 7.
Representation of key areas of recent research on Bambara groundnut (underground bean; Vigna subterranea*).*

legume for combating malnutrition. Key focus areas for the research on *P. tetragonolobus* include (1) genetic improvement and genomics (aimed at improving traits like early maturity, disease resistance, and high-yielding, determinate growth habits); (2) nutritional and functional food development (aimed at using its flour in biscuits to fight malnutrition, owing to its high seed protein content: 29%–37%, and essential amino acid content); (3) medicinal and nutraceutical properties (owing to the occurrence of bioactive compounds like phenolics and flavonoids in its leaves, roots, and pods); (4) agronomic potential and sustainability (aimed at improving soil-fertility due to its high nitrogen-fixing capacity and adaptability to tropical climates); and (5) optimization of utilization (aimed at standardizing processing techniques to reduce anti-nutritional factors and improve digestibility) [53, 54].

3.4 Marama bean

Domestication, genomic characterization, and high-value nutritional/medicinal potential are important focus areas of research on *T. esculentum*. Other key focus areas also include identifying genetic drought tolerance mechanisms, developing food applications (milk, oil), and evaluating its high-protein (30%–39%) and high-lipid (30%–43%) composition. These focus areas aim to transform this wild-harvested, drought-tolerant Southern African legume into a sustainable crop for food security [32, 44].

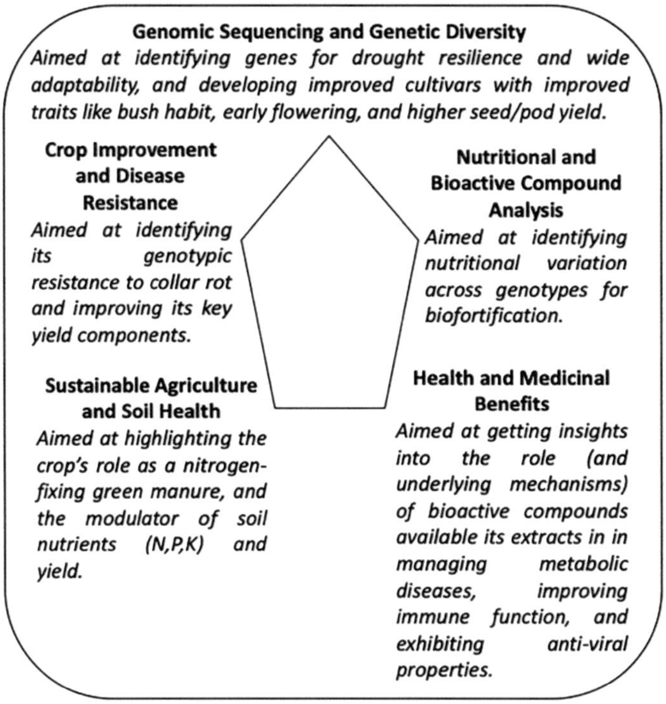

Figure 8.
*Representation of key areas of recent research on hyacinth bean (*Lablab purpureus*).*

3.5 Hyacinth bean/lablab

Recent research efforts have been made to transform the underutilized *L. purpureus* into a vital, climate-smart food source in order to improve food security, nutritional quality, and soil health. Moreover, exhaustive genomic sequencing for drought tolerance, exploring genetic diversity for higher-yielding varieties, analysing nutritional compounds, and investigating antiviral properties are the key focus areas of research on this multipurpose 'orphan' legume [40, 55, 56] (see **Figure 8**).

4. Conclusions and future prospects

This chapter made an effort to overview key insights into the origin, botany, and benefits of the selected neglected and underutilized legume crops; highlight the major constraints responsible for the neglect of these legume crops; and also briefly enlighten readers about important outcomes of recent research on these forgotten gem crops. However, future research on the above-discussed neglected and underutilized legume crops must primarily aim to transition their current status to key components of sustainable food systems, which may offer solutions for food insecurity, poverty, and climate change. Significant improvements in their climate resilience and yields can be achieved by applying advanced breeding, genomics, and omics technologies. Moreover, strengthening the value chain should also be

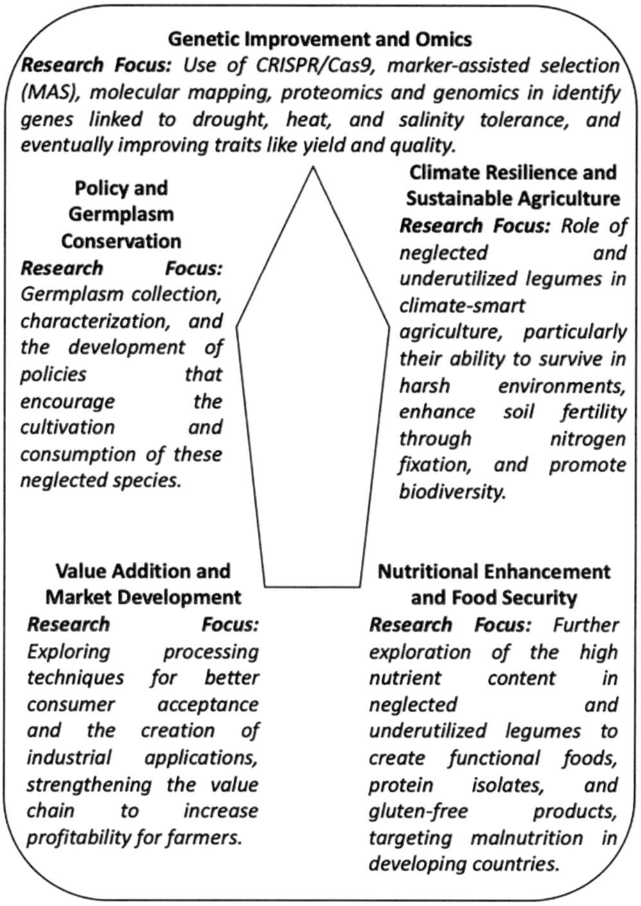

Figure 9.
Representation of key future research areas and prospects in the context of neglected and underutilized legumes.

researched to further enhance consumer acceptance, create industrial applications, and eventually increase profitability for farmers involved in the cultivation of these neglected and underutilized legume crops (see **Figure 9**).

Incorporating the highlighted, above-overlooked and/or least-explored aspects would definitely help integrate these largely ignored legume crops into mainstream agricultural systems, thereby enhancing economic viability to support food security and sustainable agriculture.

Author details

Naser A. Anjum[1*], Asim Masood[1], Iqra Khan[1], Abdul Enam[1], Tehreem Fatima[1], Rizah Akbar[1], Palaniswamy Thangavel[2], Alexander S. Lukatkin[3], Shahid Umar[4] and Nafees A. Khan[1]

1 Department of Botany, Aligarh Muslim University, Aligarh, India

2 Department of Environmental Science, Periyar University, Salem, Tamil Nadu, India

3 Department of Botany, Plant Physiology and Ecology, N.P. Ogarev Mordovia State University, Saransk, Russia

4 Department of Botany, School of Chemical and Life Sciences, Jamia Hamdard, New Delhi, India

*Address all correspondence to: naanjum1@myamu.ac.in

References

[1] Sinha V, Mondal D, Tiwari G, Shinde S, Vishvakarma NK, et al. Human nutrition: The concept of a balanced diet. In: Kumar A, Maheshwari NV, Tripathi MK, Kumar S, eds. Innovations in Ayurvedic Nutrition: Principles and Concepts. Singapore: Springer Nature Singapore; 2025. p. 29–54

[2] Zholdakova ZI, Rakhmanov RS, Bogomolova ES, Khayrov RS, Olyushina EA. The role of a balanced diet in the metabolism of nutrients. Hygiene and Sanitation. 2021;**100**(4):333–338

[3] Day L, Cakebread JA, Loveday SM. Food proteins from animals and plants: Differences in the nutritional and functional properties. Trends in Food Science and Technology. 2022;**119**:428–442

[4] Varzakas T, Smaoui S. Global food security and sustainability issues: The road to 2030 from nutrition and sustainable healthy diets to food systems change. Foods. 2024;**13**(2):306

[5] Visioli F. Redefining protein quality: Integrating health outcomes and environmental impacts in the plant-animal protein debate. Foods. 2024;**13**(24):4128

[6] Anjum NA. Book Review: Legumes under environmental stress: Yield, improvement and adaptations. Frontiers in Plant Science. 2016;7:798

[7] Maphosa Y, Jideani VA. The role of legumes in human nutrition. In: Chavari M, editor. Functional Food-Improve Health Through Adequate Food. London, United Kingdom: IntechOpen; 2017. p. 103–109

[8] Odeku OA, Ogunniyi QA, Ogbole OO, Fettke J. Forgotten gems: Exploring the untapped benefits of underutilized legumes in agriculture, nutrition, and environmental sustainability. Plants. 2024;**13**(9):1208

[9] Bhat R, Karim AA. Exploring the nutritional potential of wild and underutilized legumes. Comprehensive Reviews in Food Science and Food Safety. 2009;**8**(4):305–331

[10] Kaur K, Toor BS, Kataria A, Sasamalo MM. Potential of underutilized legumes toward nutritional security and diversity. Legume Science. 2025a;**7**(4):e70059

[11] Samal I, Bhoi TK, Raj MN, Majhi PK, Murmu S, Pradhan AK, Kumar D, et al. Underutilized legumes: Nutrient status and advanced breeding approaches for qualitative and quantitative enhancement. Frontiers in Nutrition. 2023;**10**:1110750

[12] Singh N, Jain P, Ujinwal M, Langyan S. Escalate protein plates from legumes for sustainable human nutrition. Frontiers in Nutrition. 2022;**9**:977986

[13] Nayak SP, Lone RA, Fakhrah S, Chauhan A, Sarvendra K, Mohanty CS. Mainstreaming underutilized legumes for providing nutritional security. In: Bhat R, editor. Future Foods. Cambridge, MA: Academic Press; 2022. p. 151–163

[14] Murevanhema YY, Jideani VA. Potential of Bambara groundnut (Vigna

subterranea (L.) Verdc) milk as a probiotic beverage-a review. Critical Reviews in Food Science and Nutrition. 2013;**53**(9):954–967

[15] Nwokolo E. Bambara groundnut (Vigna subterranea (L.) Verdc.). In: Nwokolo E, Smartt J, editors. Food and Feed from Legumes and Oilseeds. Boston, MA: Springer; 1996a. p. 216–221

[16] Ramatsetse KE, Ramashia SE, Mashau ME. A review on health benefits, antimicrobial and antioxidant properties of Bambara groundnut (Vigna subterranean). International Journal of Food Properties. 2023;**26** (1):91–107

[17] Adewale BD, Konyeme TE, Fayose FT, Odetoye AA, Popoola JO, Ojuederie BO, et al. Botanical and economic significance of African Yam Bean and its relatives. In: Pratap A, Singh CM, Verma DK, Mishra AK, editors. Integrated Improvement of Food Legumes. Cham: Springer Nature Switzerland; 2025. p. 299–325

[18] Potter D, Doyle JJ. Origins of the African Yam bean (Sphenostylis stenocarpa, Leguminosae): Evidence from morphology, isozymes, chloroplast DNA, and linguistics. Economic Botany. 1992;**46**:276–292

[19] Nnamani CV, Ajayi SA, Oselebe HO, Atkinson CJ, Igboabuchi AN, Ezigbo EC. Sphenostylis stenocarpa (ex. A. Rich.) Harms., a fading genetic resource in a changing climate: Prerequisite for conservation and sustainability. Plants. 2017;**6**(3):30

[20] Nwokolo E. African yam bean (Sphenostylis stenocarpa (Hoechst ex. A. Rich.) Harms). In: Nwokolo E, Smartt J, editors. Food and Feed from Legumes and Oilseeds. Boston, MA: Springer; 1996b. p. 182–188

[21] Adewale BD, Nnamani CV. Introduction to food, feed, and health wealth in African yam bean, a locked-in African indigenous tuberous legume. Frontiers in Sustainable Food Syststem. 2022;**6**:726458

[22] George TT, Obilana AO, Oyeyinka SA. The prospects of African yam bean: Past and future importance. Heliyon. 2020;**6**(11):e05458

[23] Palanga KK, Ahonon AS, Bawa A, Batchazi K, Modom Banla E, et al. Evaluation of African yam bean (Sphenostylis stenocarpa) accessions grown in Togo for nutritional and antinutritional properties. Frontiers in Food Science and Technology. 2025;**5**:1659294

[24] Sriwichai S, Monkham T, Sanitchon J, Jogloy S, Chankaew S. Dual-purpose of the winged bean (Psophocarpus tetragonolobus (L.) DC.), the neglected tropical legume, based on pod and tuber yields. Plants (Basel). 2021;**10**(8):1746

[25] Tanzi AS, Eagleton GE, Ho WK, Wong QN, Mayes S, Massawe F. Winged bean (Psophocarpus tetragonolobus (L.) DC.) for food and nutritional security: Synthesis of past research and future direction. Planta. 2019;**250**(3):911–931

[26] Yang S, Grall A, Chapman MA. Origin and diversification of winged bean (Psophocarpus tetragonolobus (L.) DC.), a multipurpose underutilized legume. American Journal of Botany. 2018;**105**(5):888–897

[27] Yadav L, Yadav A, Pratiksha, Jha AK. Psophocarpus tetragonolobus

(winged bean). In: Gupta AK, Negi PS, editors. Underutilized Tuber Crops of the Himalayan Region - Nutraceutical Potential, Processing, and Applications. United States: Academic Press; 2026. p. 409–424

[28] Chankaew S, Sriwichai S, Rakvong T, Monkham T, Sanitchon J, Tangphatsornruang S, et al. The first genetic linkage map of Winged bean (Psophocarpus tetragonolobus (L.) DC.) and QTL mapping for flower-, pod-, and seed-related traits. Plants 2022;**11**:500

[29] Chimwamurombe PM. Domestication of (Tylosema esculentum (Burchell) schreiber) (Marama bean): A work in progress in Namibia. Biosciences Biotechnology Research Asia. 2016;**8**(2):549–556

[30] Holse M, Larsen FH, Hansen Å, Engelsen SB. Characterization of Marama bean (Tylosema esculentum) by comparative spectroscopy: NMR, FT-Raman, FT-IR and NIR. Food Research International. 2011;**44**(1):373–384

[31] Omotayo AO, Aremu AO. Marama bean (Tylosema esculentum (Burch.) A. Schreib): An indigenous plant with potential for food, nutrition, and economic sustainability. Food and Function. 2021;**12**(6):2389–2403

[32] Holse M, Husted S, Hansen Å. Chemical composition of Marama bean (Tylosema esculentum) - A wild African bean with unexploited potential. Journal of Food Composition and Analysis. 2010;**23**(6):648–657

[33] Maass BL. Origin, domestication and global dispersal of Lablab purpureus (L.) Sweet (Fabaceae): Current understanding. Seed. 2016;**10**:14

[34] Subagio A. Characterization of hyacinth bean (Lablab purpureus (L.) sweet) seeds from Indonesia and their protein isolate. Food Chemistry. 2006;**95**(1):65–70

[35] Amkul K, Sookbang JM, Somta P. Genetic diversity and structure of landrace of lablab (Lablab purpureus (L.) Sweet) cultivars in Thailand revealed by SSR markers. Breeding Science. 2021;**71**(2):176–183

[36] Maass BL, Knox MR, Venkatesha SC, Angessa TT, Ramme S, Pengelly BC. Lablab purpureus - a crop lost for Africa? Tropical Plant Biology. 2010;**3**:123–135

[37] Akpapunam M. Hyacinth bean (Lablab purpureus (L.) sweet). In: Nwokolo E, Smartt J, eds. Food and Feed from Legumes and Oilseeds. Boston, MA: Springer US; 1996. p. 103–108

[38] Naeem M, Shabbir A, Aftab T, Khan MMA. Lablab bean (Lablab purpureus L.)-An untapped resilient protein reservoir. In: FarooqM, Siddique KHM, eds. Neglected and Underutilized Crops. 2023;391–411

[39] Pandey DK, Singh S, Dubey SK, Mehra TS, Dixit S, Sawargaonkar G. Nutrient profiling of lablab bean (Lablab purpureus) from north-eastern India: A potential legume for plant-based meat alternatives. Journal of Food Composition and Analysis. 2023;**119**:105252

[40] Zhou J, Wang W, Zhang Z, Zhu G, Qiao J, Guo S, Bai Y, et al. An underutilized bean: Hyacinth bean (Lablab purpureus (L.) sweet): Bioactive compounds, functional activity, and future food prospect and

applications. Journal of the Science of Food and Agriculture 2025;**105**:701–720

[41] Agyeman K, Asante BO, Berchie JN, Sarkodie-Addo J, Marno P, Adabah R. Farmers' perceptions, constraints and preferences for improved Bambara groundnut varieties in Ghana. Journal of Agriculture and Food Research. 2021;**3**:100097

[42] Majola NG, Gerrano AS, Shimelis H.Bambara groundnut (Vigna subterranea (L.) Verdc.) production, utilisation and genetic improvement in Sub-Saharan Africa. Agronomy. 2021;**11** (7):1345

[43] Lepcha P, Egan AN, Doyle JJ, Sathyanarayana N. A review on current status and future prospects of winged bean (Psophocarpus tetragonolobus) in tropical agriculture. Plant Foods and Human Nutrition. 2017;**72**(3):225–235

[44] Cullis C, Chimwamurombe P, Kunert K, Vorster J. Perspective on the present state and future usefulness of Marama bean (Tylosema esculentum). Food and Energy Security. 2023;**12**(2): e422

[45] Faria M, Mabaya E, Jordaan D. Markets for Marama beans in Southern Africa: Linking sustainable products with sustainable livelihoods. Development Southern Africa. 2011;**28**(4):477–492

[46] Abdulhamid A, Muhammad WA, Haruna TM, Ibrahim W, Abdul-Rahman M, Modu BM. Hyacinth beans (Lablab purpereus) as an emerging plant protein source for animal production: A review. Veterinary Integrative Sciences. 2026;**24**(1):1–16

[47] Khan AU, Choudhury MAR, Talucder MSA, Hossain MS, Ali S, et al. Constraints and solutions of country bean (Lablab purpureus L.) production: A review. Acta Entomology and Zoology 2020;**1**:37–45

[48] Naeem M, Shabbir A, Ansari AA, Aftab T, Khan MMA, Uddin M. Hyacinth bean (Lablab purpureus L.)- An underutilised crop with future potential. Scientia Horticulturae. 2020;**272**:109551

[49] Arshad MT, Irfan A, Ikram A, Islam M, Yupanqui CT, Zubair M, et al. Bambara groundnut (Vigna subterranea). In: Gupta AK, ed. Underutilized Seeds: Sustainable Solutions for Health, Industry, and Environment. Singapore: Springer Nature Singapore; 2026. p. 77–105

[50] Khan MMH, Rafii MY, Ramlee SI, Jusoh M, Al-Mamun M. Bambara groundnut (Vigna subterranea L. Verdc): A crop for the new millennium, its genetic diversity, and improvements to mitigate future food and nutritional challenges. Sustainability. 2021;**13**(10):5530

[51] Majola NG, Gerrano AS, Shimelis H, Mashilo J. Analyses of phytochemicals and nutritional compositions in Bambara groundnut (Vigna subterranea [L.] Verdc). Journal of Agriculture and Food Research. 2025;**19**:101610

[52] Oluwole OO, Aworunse OS, Aina AI, Oyesola OL, Popoola JO, Oyatomi OA, et al. A review of biotechnological approaches towards crop improvement in African yam bean (Sphenostylis stenocarpa Hochst. Ex A. Rich.). Heliyon. 2021;**7**(11):e08481

[53] Bassal H, Hijazi A, Farhan H, Trabolsi C, Ahmad BS, Khalil A, Maresca M, et al. Study of the

antioxidant and anti-inflammatory properties of the biological extracts of Psophocarpus tetragonolobus using two extraction methods. Molecules 2021;**26**:4435

[54] Kaur S, Mudgil D, Mudgil S, Seem K, Kumari A, Meena KK, et al. Winged bean: From underutilized legume to multi-utility crop-nutritional, phytochemical, industrial, and functional perspectives for global food security and sustainability. Applied Food Research. 2025;**5**(2):101417

[55] Kumari M, Naresh P, Acharya GC, Laxminarayana K, Singh HS, Raghu BR, Aghora TS. Nutritional diversity of Indian lablab bean (Lablab purpureus (L.) Sweet): An approach towards biofortification. South African Journal of Botany. 2022;**149**:189–195

[56] Shubha K, Choudhary AK, Dubey AK, Tripathi K, Kumar R, Kumar S, et al Evaluation of lablab bean [Lablab purpureus (L.) sweet] genotypes: Unveiling superior pod yield, nutritional quality, and collar rot resistance. Frontiers in Nutrition. 2024;**10**:1243923

Chapter 6

Underutilized and Wild Legumes: New Frontiers

Mohamed A. S. Khalifa, Asmaa H. Zaki, Ali Hassan Anany and Bahaa Abugammie

Abstract

Underutilized and wild legumes represent a critical but undervalued genetic and nutritional resource in global food systems. Despite their ecological resilience, nutritional richness, and potential contribution to sustainable agriculture, these species remain neglected, mainly in modern breeding research and commercialization. This chapter aims to highlight their significance, challenges, and strategic pathways for mainstreaming their utilization in food, medicine, and environmental management. The chapter introduces underutilized and wild legumes by exploring their diversity, classification, and distribution; examining their nutritional and functional attributes; assessing their agronomic and ecological significance; reviewing advances in breeding, genetic improvement, and biotechnology; identifying key constraints to their utilization; and outlining future research priorities and prospects.

Keywords: underutilized legumes, orphan legumes, biodiversity conservation, climate resilience, nutritional security

1. Introduction

The world's population is growing swiftly and is expected to reach 9.8 billion by 2050. To maintain global food security, food resources must be increased by 70% by that time [1]. To achieve that goal, many actions should be taken in multiple directions to develop the current agricultural systems. To achieve sustainable food security, it is necessary to incorporate newly improved crops alongside major staple crops like maize, rice, wheat, and soybeans. The Fabaceae family hosts a substantial number of uncommon species with untapped potential. It contains over 20,000 species distributed across more than 700 genera, placing it third among the most prominent families after Asteraceae and Orchidaceae. These lesser-known species are defined as underutilized, orphan, minor, niche, or wild legumes. Underutilized legumes are standard components of traditional agroecosystems across Asia, Africa, and Latin America, valued for their importance in local diets and their low-input requirements [2, 3]. Alongside the impacts of climate change on agricultural systems and the increasing demand for balanced nutritional food resources, underutilized legumes are becoming increasingly important.

Underutilized legumes gain their potential from their unique attributes compared to commonly grown plants. They have potential adaptability to climate change, improve soil biodiversity, fix atmospheric nitrogen, and grow in low-resource and marginal lands [4]. These plants have superior nutritional profiles that could reduce malnutrition and help in achieving global food security, in addition to containing bioactive compounds with multiple functions and applications [2]. Underutilized legumes are a widely diverse group of species. They are distributed across many ecological systems, which can represent a renewable resource for genetic studies seeking new traits that address issues in high-yield cultivated crops, in addition to the high expectation of improving underutilized legumes in general and making them competitive crops [5].

However, these plants have potential for the future; they are playing important roles in some local communities' food security. They face challenges related to yield productivity, consumer acceptance, and their current limited economic value, which prevent their global expansion [4]. In this chapter, we aim to examine the resilience of underutilized legumes, the challenges they face, and solutions for their future integration into agricultural systems seeking to achieve sustainable food security.

2. Diversity, classification, and distribution

Fabaceae (Leguminosae) is a vast family encompassing a broad range of life forms, from trees and shrubs to perennials and annuals. It comprises about 800 genera, ranking as the third-largest family behind Orchidaceae and Asteraceae, with approximately 20,000 species [6–8].

2.1 Germplasm conservation

2.1.1 Genetic diversity conserved in ex situ germplasm collections and its characterization

N.I. Vavilov was *the first to conserve legumes through ex situ* conservation in 1926. Legumes represent the second-largest *ex situ* germplasm collection, accounting for over 15% of total collections, second only to cereals [9]. The study of genetic diversity for both germplasm management and breeding has garnered significant attention, particularly since Frankel [10] introduced the concept of a core collection [10]. The conserved germplasm is characterized not only by morphological traits but also by chemical components and stress tolerances. The Global Crop Trust (GCT) promotes crop improvement, including legumes, while supporting gene banks in *ex situ* conservation efforts through a range of strategies, such as regeneration, collection of crop wild relatives (CWR), evaluation, and pre-breeding [11]. It is critical to conserve legume landraces in gene banks to mitigate the effects of climate change and genetic erosion caused by urban expansion [12]. These landraces are vital for legume improvement because they may have undergone natural selection for stress tolerance [13, 14].

The availability of germplasm resources databases for international research centers and national gene banks will allow online requests for accessions across countries globally for the selection of multi-trait accessions and multi-location evaluation. Nowadays, the greatest challenge for gene banks is the high cost of phenotyping, so research could overcome this by using a single seed per accession for advanced genotyping and phenotyping to explore the diversity stored in germplasm collections [14, 15].

2.1.2 Botanical gardens and herbaria as sources of information and complementary conservation

Botanical gardens play a crucial role in the *ex situ* conservation of seeds, complementing gene bank efforts. They face both challenges and opportunities; to mitigate climate change, they must prioritize endangered species, e.g., CWR. Moreover, botanical gardens have historically contributed to the evaluation of new germplasm [16]. For many years, they have maintained excellent herbarium collections, such as those at the Royal Botanic Gardens, Kew, UK. These herbaria provide precious resources for assessing CWR diversity, accessing valuable information for gene banks, and conducting gap analyses to identify conservation shortfalls, as demonstrated in studies on *Phaseolus* [17] and *Lathyrus* [18].

2.1.3 In situ conservation of legumes

In situ genetic reserve conservation involves identifying, designating, managing, and monitoring genetic diversity within natural wild populations in dedicated areas under active, long-term protection [19]. There are many advantages to *in situ* conservation. For instance, it improves the evolution of legume CWR diversity under stress, but the difficulty lies in identifying the required traits for legume breeders, both currently and in the future. Without regeneration and efficient management, natural variation within the population could disappear, or the population could be lost entirely [20]. Maxted [21] made the first recommendation for establishing *in situ* genetic reserves for legume CWR diversity, proposing four locations in Syria and Turkey to conserve Fabeae species [21]. Later, the Global Environment Facility (GEF) project in Turkey created three such reserves, with Ceylanpınar (a state agricultural farm and genetic reserve in Şanlıurfa Province) prioritizing *in situ* conservation of legume (and cereal) CWR [22, 23]. The recommended sites in Syria's Suwayda Province by Maxted (1995) have been developed for *in situ* legume conservation [24, 25]. Further genetic reserves for legume CWR have been established in Nevada, United States, for *Lathyrus grimesii* Barneby, and in Costa Rica for wild bean populations (*Phaseolus* spp.) [26].

2.2 Classification and geographical distribution

The Fabaceae family consists of six subfamiles and numerous key tribes, with fabea being one of the most significant (**Table 1**). There are five accepted genera in the tribe Fabeae [7, 27]: *Lathyrus* L. (about 160 species); *Lens* Mill. (4 species); *Pisum* L. (2–3 species); *Vicia* L. (160–200 species); and the monotypic genus *Vavilovia* Fed. This tribe is a sister to the Trifolieae tribe [27, 28]. The Fabeae tribe can be morphologically characterized by paripinnate, often tendril-bearing leaves, and a pubescent style or pollen brush [29].

3. Nutritional and functional attributes

Underutilized legume crops are considered a key solution to narrowing the food gap at present and in the future [47]. They are among the most crucial plant-based protein sources, serve as a cost-effective food resource, and rank after cereals in

Genus	Approx. no. of species	Main geographical distribution/ center of diversity	Major cultivated species/notes	References
Lathyrus	~160	Europe, Asia, and North America extend to South America and East Africa	*Lathyrus sativus* (grass pea)	[27, 30, 31]
Vicia	160–200	Southern Europe; Mediterranean; West and Central Asia; China; East Asia; India	*Vicia sativa* (common vetch)	[7]
Pisum	2–3	European–Mediterranean region; Middle and Northwest Asia; Fertile Crescent; Central Asia	*Pisum sativum*	[7]
Lens	4	Turkey to Uzbekistan (wild relatives)	*Lens culinaris* subsp. *culinaris*	[32, 33]
Vavilovia	1 (monotypic)	Western Asia (closely related to the Fabeae region)	Wild genus	[34]
Medicago	87	Widely distributed; associated with the Trifolieae tribe	*Medicago sativa* (Alfalfa)	[35]
Trifolium	~255	Cosmopolitan; mostly Northern Hemisphere	Clover species	[36, 37]
Cicer	~43	Southeastern Turkey and Northern Syria (origin)	*Cicer arietinum* (chickpea)	[38–40]
Phaseolus	76	New World: center of diversity in Mexico	*P. vulgaris, P. lunatus, P. coccineus, P. acutifolius*	[41, 42]
Vigna	~150	Old and New Worlds; warm temperate and tropical regions	V. radiata, V. mungo, V. angularis	[43, 44]
Glycine	~22	East Asia (subgenus Soja); wild species, mainly in Australia	*Glycine max* (soybean)	[45, 46]
Cajanus	~13 genera in subtribe; ~ 17 spp. in genus	Tropical and subtropical regions (origin in India)	*Cajanus cajan* (pigeonpea)	[6, 7]

Table 1.
Classification and geographical distribution of key legume genera.

addressing the food security crisis [48]. Furthermore, they are rich sources; in addition to protein and amino acids, they provide significant amounts of vitamins, minerals, fiber, carbohydrates, and bioactive compounds, with a variety of physiological and nutritional benefits [49, 50].

3.1 Comparative nutritional composition

Underutilized legumes are highly nutritious and affordable sources that can improve health and food security, especially amid growing concerns about the impact of animal proteins on health and the environment [51, 52]. Studies on species from underutilized legumes such as Bambara groundnut, jack bean, lima bean, sword bean, woolly senna, and velvet bean have shown that they provide remarkable amounts of protein, dietary fibers, lipids, carbohydrates, and key minerals such as calcium, phosphorus, sodium, potassium, iron, zinc, manganese, and magnesium, demonstrating their capacity to meet human nutritional demands [53–55].

Many underutilized legumes have multiple edible parts, broadening their dietary options and making them more readily accepted across different dishes and serving methods. Examples include marama bean, zombie pea, and African yam bean (AYB), which produce both edible seeds or grains and underground tubers [56, 57]; fenugreek, which provides edible seeds and leaves [58]; and winged bean, where flowers, seeds, pod cases, immature pods, tuberous roots, and leaves are all edible [59].

Detailed analysis of specific underutilized legumes demonstrated their nutritional diversity and richness. Seeds of *Bauhinia malabarica* contain crude lipids dominated by unsaturated oleic and linoleic acids, and a protein profile rich with about 45% glutamic acid, supporting the overall protein quality [60]; *Vigna aconitifolia* and *Vigna vexillata* seeds contain high protein and minerals, with *V. aconitifolia* having higher crude fat and a better unsaturated fatty acids profile [61]; analysis of *Canavalia* species seeds showed the presence of substantial digestible starch, fatty acids, and dietary fiber, alongside high protein content (31.8–36.0%) with variable levels of the non-proteinogenic amino acid, canavanine [61]. While canavanine plays a role in plant defenses and is expected to have pharmaceutical benefits for the human body, it poses a risk of toxicity at high consumption levels [62].

Underutilized legumes hold adequate levels of vitamins and minerals. They provide thiamine (B1), riboflavin (B2), niacin (B3), pantothenic acid (B5), pyridoxine (B6), vitamin A, vitamin C, vitamin D, vitamin E, and vitamin K, alongside Na, Ca, Cu, Mg, Mn, P, K, and Zn, supporting development, immunity, metabolism, memory, and blood circulation [63–66]. Protein amino acid profiles from underutilized legumes have shown bioactivity, boosting the immune system function, metabolic regulation, glucose, and fatty acid processes [67, 68].

Anti-nutritional factors, alongside allergenicity and digestibility, are considered significant constraints on their functional utilization. Nevertheless, studies have shown that a variety of processing techniques, including fermentation, high-pressure cooking, boiling, and irradiation, may overcome these challenges [48, 69, 70].

3.2 Bioactive compounds and functional properties

Bioactive compounds are substances that have physiological effects on living organisms [71, 72]. Legumes, including the underutilized species, are considered a rich source of diverse bioactive compounds such as polyphenols, tannins, alkaloids, saponins, terpenoids, bioactive peptides, omega-3 fatty acids, flavonoids, carotenoids, and anthocyanins (see **Table 2**). These compounds exhibit a broad spectrum of functional properties, including antioxidant, anticancer, antitumor, anti-inflammatory, antimicrobial, and neuroprotective activities [73, 74].

Several studies on the bioactive compounds of underutilized legumes, such as winged bean, Kersting's groundnut, Bambara groundnut, and AYB, suggest that these compounds are capable of enhancing human health as nutraceuticals [66, 75–77] by improving digestion, protecting against oxidative stress, supporting weight management, and reducing the risk of cardiovascular diseases [78–80].

Underutilized legumes	Bioactive compounds	Positive health properties	References
Bambara Groundnut (*Vigna subterranea*)	α-Tocopherol, total polyphenols, Trolox equivalent, antioxidant capacity, ferric reducing antioxidant power (FRAP), condensed tannins, flavonoids	Antitumor, neuroprotective, antioxidant, anti-nutritional, and cardioprotective activities	[65, 70, 82, 86, 87]
Rice bean (*Vigna umbellata*)	Phenolics: p-coumaric acid, epicatechin, catechin, flavonoids, quercetin, isovitexin, sinapic acid, vitexin, ferulic acid	Antidiabetic properties, antioxidant activity	[88–91]
Lima bean (*Phaseolus lunatus*)	Cyanide, thio-glucosides, bioactive flavonoids, anthocyanins, trypsin inhibitors, saponins, cyanine, hemagglutinin, producing glucosides, alkaloids, tannins, and oxalates	Antioxidant, anticancer, anti-hepatoprotective, antidiabetic, antifungal, anti-nutritional, and hypocholesterolaemic activities	[92–95]
Stinky bean (*Parkia speciosa*)	Polyphenols, flavonoids, alkaloids, and terpenoids	Antioxidant activity, anti-nutritional activity, and hypoglycemic activity	[96, 97]
Adzuki bean (*Vigna angularis*)	Epicatechin 7-O-β-D-glucopyranoside (E7G), flavonoids: procyanidins B-1, catechin 7-β-D-glucopyranoside (C7G), malvidin-3-O-glucoside – O-glucoside and B-3, peonidin-3-rutinoside, phenolic acids: ferulic acid, caffeic acid, and catechin	Antihyperglycemic, hypochloremia effects, anti-atherogenic antioxidant, and anti-thrombogenic activity	[90, 98–100]
Horse gram (*Macrotyloma uniflorum*)	Phenolic compounds, polysaccharides, anthocyanins, and flavonoids	Anti-obesity, anti-inflammatory, cardioprotective, anticancer, antioxidant, neuroprotective, and antimicrobial activity	[101, 102]
African Yam Bean (AYB) (*Sphenostylis stenocarpa*)	Trypsin inhibitor, phytate, tannin, oxalate, flavonoids, alkaloids, phenols, non-starch polysaccharides, slowly digestible starch (SDS), and resistant starch	Stabilizes insulin levels and glucose metabolism, enhances antioxidant activities, modulates appetite, and improves mental performance	[70, 85, 103–105]

Table 2.
Bioactive compounds found in underutilized legumes and their positive effects on human health.

The richness of underutilized legumes in polyphenol bioactive compounds gives them nutritional advantages. Polyphenols exhibit multiple physiological effects, including antimicrobial, antiviral, anti-inflammatory, antioxidant, and antimutagenic properties, mainly due to their ability to scavenge free radical molecules [81–83]. Several studies have also confirmed the anticancer potential of these compounds. For instance, ellagic acid, quercetin, catechin, and phenolic acids have been shown to prevent various cancers affecting the lungs, liver, skin, mammary glands, colon, stomach, oral cavity, and duodenum [82, 84]. Studies show that polyphenol levels in underutilized legumes are not uniform, with some species being a rich source. Among nine underutilized legumes evaluated by Ade-Omowaye et al. [83], the AYB showed high total polyphenol content and antioxidant activity. Similarly, jack bean has been reported to hold a considerable level of polyphenols, associated with numerous health benefits [83, 85].

In plants, these bioactive compounds play a crucial role in the plant defense mechanisms against herbivores, insect pests, and pathogens. Additionally, they serve as internal signaling molecules in adaptive mechanisms, as external signaling agents to attract pollinators, and in plant-to-plant communication [106, 107].

3.3 Traditional and emerging food uses

Underutilized plants provide an excellent opportunity to vary diets with healthier meals while respecting local food customs and boosting meal diversity. Beyond their gastronomic appeal, these crops offer tremendous promise for alleviating poverty and malnutrition, boosting agro-biodiversity, and aiding agricultural and nutritional development. For example, integrating underutilized foods into diets has been found to improve macro- and micronutrient deficiencies, especially iron insufficiency, among mothers and children in Kenya [108]. Similarly, forgotten crops have helped alleviate food and nutrition insecurity and hidden hunger in Burkina Faso [109]. Moreover, studies have shown that underutilized legumes possess a lower-glycemic index (GI) [110], which may significantly contribute to the prevention and treatment of several health diseases, including type 2 diabetes, by enhancing glycemic and lipid control [111], hyperlipidemia via lowering total and LDL cholesterol levels [112], and hypertension, which may be mitigated by lowering blood pressure, lipid levels, waist circumference, and body weight [113]. Underutilized legumes are abundant in soluble fiber, inherently low in fat, and cholesterol-free; consequently, they may help lower the incidence of diet-related chronic illnesses, such as malignancies [114, 115].

4. Agronomic and ecological significance

Orphan legume plants belong to the highly diverse Fabaceae family. These plants have potential due to their unique biological characteristics and interactions with the environment. This section highlights their agronomic benefits and ecological importance, underscoring their potential to support sustainable farming systems and biodiversity.

4.1 Agronomic performance and yield

Orphan legumes' yield per hectare is limited compared to other common legumes, which have gained much attention for breeding and improvements over decades. For example, Kersting's groundnut (*Macrotyloma geocarpum*) showed wide productivity variation, ranging from 25.1 kg ha^{-1} to 1,353 kg ha^{-1} [116]. Globally, pigeon pea (*Cajanus cajan*) occupies a cultivation area of 6.99 million ha^{-1}, yielding 5.96 million tons at 852 kg ha^{-1} [59]. Horse gram (*Macrotyloma uniflorum* [Lam.] Verdc.) during 2019–2020 had land cultivation in India spanning 457,000 hectares, with productivity ranging from 283 kg ha^{-1} to 649 kg ha^{-1} [117]. Bambara groundnut (*Vigna subterranea*) long-term African production data showed yields ranging from 500 kg ha^{-1} to 3,000 kg ha^{-1} [118], with yields less than 100 kg ha^{-1} in some fields [119]. Orphan legumes may not yield much per ha^{-1} in comparison to the dominant cultivated legumes like soybean. Still, their value shines through their adaptability across diverse environments, their outperformance of common legumes in marginal and low-resource lands, their importance for food security, and their potential to yield more with greater attention from institutions and researchers.

4.2 Stress tolerance and adaptation resilience

Orphan legumes are predominantly produced by smallholder farmers who mainly practice subsistence farming due to their resilience across diverse agroecological conditions, nitrogen fixation, weed control, disease control, high nutritional value, and ability to yield with low available resources, where other well-developed crops cannot. Currently, orphan legumes are gaining greater attention from researchers for their potential to support food security and sustainable agriculture [68, 120]. Environmental factors have been influencing agricultural production and affecting food security worldwide. Decision-makers, organizations, institutions, and researchers are actively working to mitigate the impact of climate change on agriculture. Orphan legumes, with their potential and performance in unsuitable conditions, could be part of the solution.

Studies on moth bean (*Vigna aconitifolia*) over two decades, from germplasm collection and evaluation, have revealed that moth bean germplasm includes accessions that tolerate heat and drought and yield well compared to other common legumes under these conditions. Additional studies focused on the nutritional profile and chemical composition to provide further knowledge of the crop and highlight opportunities for its improvement [121]. It performs well in harsh conditions and achieves optimal growth between 25 °C and 37 °C with annual rainfall of about 250–500 mm, and a yield ranging from 70 to 270 kg ha^{-1} compared to soybean, which typically requires 400–700 mm of total water to achieve optimal yields of around 3,000 kg ha^{-1}. However, growers using new improved hybrids in the USA and Australia have achieved yields of 2,600 kg ha^{-1}, indicating the ability of this crop to compete with common legumes in many aspects, with rational future investment [121, 122].

Grass pea (*Lathyrus sativus* L.), a drought-tolerant legume, can thrive in both arid and waterlogged conditions and yield 500–1,500 kg ha^{-1}. Grass pea has a deep rooting system that stabilizes soils and reduces erosion [123]. In addition, grass pea is nutritionally rich in protein, lysine, and iron. However, the presence of ODAP (0.1–2.5 g Kg^{-1} DM), a neurotoxin, primarily limits its usage [124]. The ODAP toxin can be mitigated through food processing practices such as soaking and boiling, as well as through new breeding programs [125].

Mung bean (*Vigna radiata*) plants can survive in saline conditions through a symbiotic relationship with *Rhizobium* and a beneficial relationship with *Pseudomonas,* which produce ACC deaminase, an ethylene precursor breaker, and auxin compounds that mitigate the effects of salinity on plants [126]. Pigeon pea (*Cajanus cajan*) can survive in saline soil conditions and drought with the help of a symbiotic relationship with *Bradyrhizobium* species, including *Bradyrhizobium elkanii* and *Bradyrhizobium japonicum* [127].

4.3 Drought stress and tolerance mechanisms

Plants cope with drought stress through morphological or physiological adaptive mechanisms, including leaf reduction, stomatal closure, changes in shoot-to-root biomass allocation, and root attributes [4]. In addition to general mechanisms, legumes under drought stress develop unique root systems. In comparison to other crops, legumes' rooting is greater in depth and biomass. Root meta-xylem vessels have larger diameters and a more uniform distribution in legume root systems, impacting root hydraulic conductivity and improving water uptake efficiency under drought stress. This could explain why the chickpea (*Cicer arietinum*) root system performed better than the barley (*Hordeum vulgare*) root system, with high root length density [128]. In the case of the tepary bean (*Phaseolus acutifolius*), some lines expressed significant root biomass in the deep soil profile [129].

Marama bean (*Tylosema esculentum*) can grow in desert lands, although it is not drought-tolerant. The plant avoids drought stress by storing water and assimilates in its root tubers. If it passes the vegetative growth period without stress, it stores enough in the root system to withstand possible drought waves and completes its life cycle [4, 130]. Grass pea (*Lathyrus sativus* L.) can produce yield where other crops fail under the same conditions. Grass pea matures early to escape drought, reduces leaf area, decreases stomatal conductance, and lowers flower and pod production [131, 132].

Bambara plant (*Vigna subterranea*) tolerates drought considerably and can grow under adverse environmental conditions. It performs well in regions receiving less than 500 mm of annual rainfall [133]. The crop can grow well across a range of soils with limited resources, from light loams to heavy soils, though optimal growth is achieved in sandy loam soils with a pH around 6 [134]. The pigeon pea root system harbors a wide range of microorganisms. In a study by Jain et al. in north-western India, they found that most rhizobia strains were ammonia producers, and less than 20% of the 55 isolated strains were phosphate solubilizers. All strains produced IAA when tested *in vitro*, with varying amounts across strains. Most of the 55 strains showed positive growth in acidic media.

In contrast, at salinities above 3% NaCl, strains struggled to grow, and at 8% NaCl, a few strains showed growth. At high-temperature stress above 40 °C, about 20% of strains showed good growth, while a few did so at 4 °C. In the drought tolerance test using polyethylene glycol (PEG) in the growth media, all strains showed positive growth at 10% PEG, whereas approximately 15% maintained positive growth at 20% PEG. These findings could help explain the pigeon pea's ability to withstand semi-arid and arid regions [59].

4.4 Nitrogen fixation and soil enrichment

With the global issue of climate change and the global population expected to reach 9.7 billion by 2050, ensuring food security has become more complicated. Regenerative agriculture is one of the approaches that could mitigate the issue. Under pressure from high-yield demand, chemical fertilizers, and a few used crops, land is degraded and vulnerable to factors that lower its productivity. The regenerative approach aims to restore soil health and sustainably maintain its productivity. Legume plants, with their dual benefits of providing nutritional resources and restoring soil ecology, play a pivotal role in regenerative agriculture [135, 136].

Legumes provide nutritional benefits, and many members of the family can support climate resilience and regenerative agriculture. This could be achieved through nitrogen fixation, which can reach 200 kg ha^{-1}, increasing soil organic matter, enhancing water-holding capacity, and improving soil ecology, all of which contribute to restoring or enhancing soil health. Approximately 25% yield improvement could be achieved in crop system rotation [125]. Cowpea (*Vigna unguiculata*), for example, can compete with the common crop soybean in terms of its beneficial impacts on soil and can decrease the use of artificial fertilizers by 30 to 50% through the symbiotic nitrogen fixation process [125]. Bambara groundnut (*Vigna subterranea*) has a symbiotic relationship with rhizobia and fixes approximately 150–200 kg N ha^{-1}, on par with soybean, and can be grown in marginal soils that soybean cannot [137, 138]. In intercropping systems with cereals, Bambara groundnut can increase cereal yield by 15–20% in water-limited regions [68]. Winged bean (*Psophocarpus tetragonolobus*) is a versatile crop that can grow in humid conditions and in poor soil. The seeds provide 30–40% protein and 100–200 μg/100 g folate [139]. This plant can fix 100–150 kg h^{-1} nitrogen and increase the yield of the subsequent crop by 10–15% [140]. Grass pea (*Lathyrus sativus* L.) is one of the drought-tolerant legumes capable of thriving under both arid and waterlogged conditions [141]. It has a unique root system that can stabilize soil and reduce erosion by 15–20% [123]. Pigeon pea has the potential to maintain soil fertility by fixing approximately 40 kg N ha^{-1} during one cropping season [59]. Biodiversity net gain (BNG) plant cropping strategies take many forms; the plant could be grown as a standalone crop or intercropped with cereals or other legumes [137]. BNG has a nitrogen-fixation capacity of 32–82 kg h^{-1}. Even though the amount of nitrogen is not high when compared to other legumes, the amount is estimated chiefly from the available landrace varieties that have raw potential for improvement [142].

Legumes fix atmospheric nitrogen to meet their own nutritional requirements while also benefiting associated crops [143]. In cropping sequences, nitrogen can be made available naturally through the decomposition of organic matter, mineralization, microorganisms, and the root exudates from plants, which enhance the process [144]. In intercropping systems between legumes and cereals, such as bambara groundnut and maize, observations suggest that there is an expectation of a process of nitrogen transfer between the legume plant and the cereal one, positively impacting the latter's yield. Still, the available data is not sufficient to explain this fully [145]. In rotation systems between legumes and cereals, the yield of maize after pigeon peas increased by 75–200%, as reported by Adjei-Nsiah [146].

Orphan legumes thrive on marginal lands due to their ability to stimulate colonization of different types of microorganisms that provide resources against the unfavorable conditions. Orphan legume diversity is accompanied by rhizosphere microorganism diversity. Using such crops for soil amelioration is key to organic agriculture [147]. Pigeon pea from India's semi-arid areas was found to have a habitat-wide range of nodulating *Rhizobium*, *Mesorhizobium*, and *Sinorhizobium*. These bacteria, besides nitrogen fixation, can also produce compounds that have plant growth-promoting (PGP) activities. Through further studies, these isolates could be exploited to inoculate legumes with previously characterized bacteria to ameliorate a targeted issue [59].Evaluation of rhizobia strains from the pigeon pea rhizosphere showed that most strains produce ammonia, which enhances plant growth while inhibiting plant-pathogenic microbes. Also, some strains showed the ability to solubilize phosphate, a crucial trait for enhancing plant root system development and architecture [59].

4.5 Ecosystem services and biodiversity

Plant-based biocontrol agents' usage is currently expanding to meet the needs of climate-resilient agriculture and food safety. Plants that contain phytochemicals have the potential to be used as biopesticides, capturing the attention of researchers to address this gap. Underutilized legumes are considered a rich source of diverse phytochemicals that could be used against a broad spectrum of plant pathogens.

Pyrenes and coumarins isolated from underutilized legumes have been demonstrated to exhibit antifungal activity against *Alternaria solani*, the cause of early blight [148]. Flavonoids and isoflavonoids showed potent inhibitory effects against the rust disease agent, *Gymnosporangium yamadae* Miyabe [149]. Lectins and polypeptides derived from underutilized legumes have been reported to suppress *Pseudomonas syringae* bacteria, the cause of blast and black pit in citrus [150]. Phenolic compounds present in many members exhibited antagonistic activity against the soilborne fungus causing *Fusarium* wilt in several crops, *Fusarium oxysporum* [151]. Saponins have been shown to possess inhibitory efficacy toward *Penicillium italicum*, the pathogen responsible for blue mold disease in postharvest systems [152]. Steroidal compounds isolated from underutilized legumes displayed antifungal activity against *Colletotrichum musae*, which causes anthracnose disease (dark spots, blights, and cankers on leaves, stems, flowers, and fruits) in many plants [153]. Tannins positively suppressed the pathogen associated with leaf blight disease, *Curvularia lunata* [154]. These findings underscore underutilized legumes as a rich source of eco-friendly botanical biocontrol agents for sustainable plant disease management strategies [68].

Heavy metals like Cd, Hg, Pb, Zn, P, and Cr, when present at trace concentrations, can play a positive role in plant growth and development by serving as cofactors for numerous enzymes involved in key physiological and metabolic processes. In contrast, excessive presence and accumulation beyond the critical threshold cause phytotoxicity and impaired plant growth and development. These heavy metals represent a significant global environmental concern. Bioremediation is extremely important in integrative agriculture. Species belonging to Fabaceae exhibit attributes for phytoremediation of heavy metals in contaminated soils. Hyacinth bean (*Lablab purpureus* L.) has been reported to exhibit degrees of tolerance to several heavy metals, like Cd, Hg, Pb, Zn, P, and Cr. For this reason, it is used in metal-enriched soils to enhance soil fertility and support agricultural productivity [155]. Underutilized legumes such as jack bean (*Canavalia ensiformis*) have been shown to be capable of growing in highly contaminated soil containing over 120 mg dm^{-3} [156]. The use of jack bean (*Canavalia ensiformis*) as a precursor plant for a mainstream crop, such as tobacco, yielded multiple benefits. Besides indirectly increasing tobacco yield quality, soil characteristics, such as exchangeable cations and organic matter, improved, and the impact persisted into the fourth season after planting jack bean [157]. At the mining sites of Saint-Laurent-le-Minier, in France, the soil contains high levels of heavy metals such as Zn, Cd, and lead (Pb), representing some of the most polluted areas in Europe. The use of legumes (*Anthyllis vulneraria)* and Poaceae (*Festuca*, *Koeleria* spp.) plants restores vegetative cover and limits the hazardous impact of heavy metals in the area. Further investigations revealed that the kidney vetch (*A. vulneraria*) from that site could tolerate higher levels of heavy metals than ecotypes from other sites due to its symbiotic relationship with *Mesorhizobium metallidurans* [158].

5. Breeding, genetic improvement, and biotechnological approaches

Despite their nutritional and agronomic potential, underutilized legumes such as Bambara groundnut and AYB contribute little to food systems due to socioeconomic and biological constraints. The main productivity issues include photoperiod sensitivity, protracted maturity periods, high levels of anti-nutritional factors, seed coat hardness, low seed yield, and poor postharvest shelf life [159]. These restrictions, along with dwindling farmer enthusiasm, have impeded systematic agricultural development initiatives and limited uptake. Even though these crops are known to be important, there are still few systematic breeding initiatives. Preliminary morphological and molecular characterization investigations have served as the foundation for genetic improvement attempts. Unlocking the breeding potential of these legumes requires an understanding of their genetic architecture, variety, and evolutionary connections with related species [160, 161].

5.1 Current state of germplasm research

Phenotypic and genotypic characterization is considered the most prevalent method for evaluating changes in plant research [84, 162]. The phenotypic technique is widely used to identify duplicates, detect distinctive traits, and select germplasm with advantageous characteristics [163, 164]. Although the environment may influence phenotypic investigations [165], they may also be subjective and time-consuming because they depend on visual identification [166]. On the other hand, genotypic characterization is environment-independent and selectively neutral [167]. Furthermore, Mayes et al. [137] indicated that the yield of underutilized legumes is influenced by soil characteristics and climatic variables, including temperature and rainfall. Genotype–environment interactions (GEI) cause distinct plant accessions to respond differently to each characteristic. Many farmers cultivated landraces that exhibited segregation, leading to seasonal production fluctuations, and were deficient in farmer-desired qualities such as excellent palatability and rapid processing [168]. Consequently, novel and improved cultivars are necessary to meet commercial requirements and address ecological limitations. Enhancing underutilized legume production is essential to validate its use in various cropping systems. This strategy will also benefit breeders and farmers by providing critical baseline data on established lines. It will also assist in describing desirable germplasm for breeding projects and in increasing selection efficiency under different environmental conditions. Therefore, multi-environment trials (METs) are vital for selecting high-yielding crop varieties appropriate for specific settings. Yet, the adaptation of specific genotypes to diverse environments may be gene-specific [169]. Nonetheless, it is essential to enhance the efficiency of existing breeding practices to sustain production gains amid increasing climatic variability [170].

5.2 Conventional breeding strategies

Regarding crop yield, architecture, maturity duration, and dietary value, genetic and breeding efforts to enhance neglected and underused legume crops have not achieved the desired level [171]. Despite exploring classical hybridization and other breeding approaches for specific desired purposes, the anticipated results have not yet materialized. On underused legumes, only a few successful crosses have been documented so far; for instance, a few achievements have been reported on *Cajanus cajan* and other species [172]. However, many underutilized legumes have recognized reproductive limitations, including embryo abortion, as barriers to genetic advancement. The categorization of Dolichos bean according to photoperiod susceptibility has been examined using molecular characterization by SSR markers [173].

Some phenological and morphological properties, including biological yield, 100-seed weight, plant height, days to flowering, flower color, pod curvature, number of flower buds, number of pods per plant, seed number, hypocotyl color, node numbers, pod cross-section, growth habit, and seed number per pod, exhibited notable variations in most of the underutilized species, which is essential for the production rate indication for purposes of breeding [174]. Reproductive and morpho-physiological properties are constant in a variety of legumes [175–177]. Monogenic features such as shape, texture, color, and the presence or absence of particular qualities are effectively regulated by traditional breeding procedures, whereas multigenic features (quantitative traits) such as tolerance to abiotic stressors and plant production are significantly impacted by environment–genetic interactions, which are less accurate and time-consuming in breeding procedures [178]. To estimate the fraction of phenotypic variation within a population, plant breeders use narrow-sense heritability (NSH) as an additive genetic effect [179].

5.3 Genomic and molecular tools

Genomic selection (GS) is considered one of the most advanced genetic breeding strategies. Genomic Selection uses genome-wide markers to forecast breeding values, enabling the selection of genotypes with complex quantitative traits, including drought tolerance, yield stability, and multi-stress resistance [180]. The alternatives to promote drought tolerance in grain legumes using biotechnology-driven methods include GS, epigenetic variation, marker-assisted recurrent selection, transgenics, and genome editing [181]. The benefits of GS include early-generation selection without phenotyping, thereby improving genetic gain per unit time. However, GS has been deployed in chickpea and lentil for forecasting grain production and drought response, utilizing genomic prediction models with great accuracy. Genomic selection is projected to become an essential component of legume breeding pipelines. However, genomics-dependent techniques are considered critical for improving underused legumes; thus, the use of next-generation sequencing (NGS) and crop genomics has advanced significantly over the last decade [182]. Next-generation sequencing may be utilized to sequence the genes associated with nutrients in neglected crops to meet this requirement [183]. The genes linked to nutrient buildup may be identified in whole-genome sequencing (WGS) databases and used in breeding strategies [184].

Moreover, high-throughput techniques, such as single-nucleotide polymorphisms (SNPs), have become possible through improved DNA sequencing, making their use in crop breeding easier. Diversity arrays technology (DArT) is fundamental, as it can generate genome-wide SNPs in organisms without requiring prior knowledge of DNA sequences [185, 186]. The DArT technology is effective in genetic research of various legumes, including pigeon peas [187], AYB [188], common beans [189], and bambara groundnuts [190]. Furthermore, the field of plant breeding focuses on identifying and utilizing genetic diversity [167] and on monitoring potential DNA markers and areas linked to desirable characteristics [191, 192]. However, characterization based on phenotypic traits and genotypic data can be used independently or in conjunction, as no single characterization approach is superior to the others [193], and no method has been found sufficient to evaluate a target aspect of a species [194, 195].

5.4 Transcriptomics methods for quantitative and qualitative improvement

About 20 years ago, serial analysis of gene expression (SAGE), microarrays, and northern blot hybridization were the only technologies used to measure gene expression levels. The situation has substantially improved owing to developments in analytical tools and NGS technology [196]. RNA sequencing has replaced gene expression studies by the sequencing of cDNA [197]. This is one of the most effective approaches, frequently used to evaluate genes that are nutrient-responsive and associated with adaptation. For instance, transcriptomic analysis of two horse gram genotypes differing in drought tolerance identified many transcription factor families, including MYB, NAC, and WRKY, as contributors to drought stress resistance [198]. Furthermore, another study based on transcriptome investigation comparing mungbean yellow mosaic virus (MYMV) susceptibility and resistant genotypes identified critical genes like *lipoxygenase (LOX), jasmonate ZIM-domain (JAZ)* , *cytochrome P450*, and *phytoene synthase*, which led to the development of resistance toward the virus [199]. Overall, these advances demonstrate that RNA-sequencing–based transcriptomic analyses provide a robust and reliable framework for identifying key genes and regulatory networks underlying stress adaptation and disease resistance in plants.

5.5 Case studies of successful genetic improvement

Several studies have reported successful genetic improvement in different underutilized legumes. Pigeon pea has considerable potential for harnessing hybrid vigor owing to its partial outcrossing characteristics [200]. The identification of male sterility mechanisms in pigeonpea constituted a significant advancement by obviating the need for physical emasculation and facilitating hybrid seed production. Despite the initial investigation of genetic male sterility (GMS), its practical constraints in extensive hybrid seed production led to its abandonment. Cytoplasmic-nuclear male sterility (CMS), which is maternally inherited, has shown greater efficiency and economic viability for hybrid breeding. Cytoplasmic-nuclear male sterility systems have been documented in over 150 plant species, including various legumes such as soybean, common bean, pigeonpea, and faba bean [201–203]. Continuous breeding efforts in pigeonpea have led to the discovery of several cytoplasmic male sterility (CMS) sources and the development of enhanced cultivars, culminating in the release of over 140 varieties in India within the last 50 years across many agroecological zones [204].

In contrast, genetic improvement efforts in other underutilized legumes remain limited. For instance, no successful breeding lines have yet been documented in AYB [205], although recent research employing partial *rbcL* sequences has identified several polymorphic and haplotype regions that may serve as potential candidates for mutation breeding and marker-assisted selection [206]. Similarly, Majola (2023) [207] analyzed production limits, genetic resources, and breeding techniques in

Bambara groundnut, resulting in the formation of novel breeding populations with increased yield and nutritional quality for variety release and adoption in South Africa [3]. Collectively, these case studies demonstrate both successes and existing gaps in genetic improvement efforts, underscoring the need for combined breeding and molecular techniques to expedite the development of underexploited legume crops [208].

6. Constraints and barriers to utilization

The resilience of orphan legumes arises from their potential to play a remarkable role in integrative agriculture. They can provide new nutritional resources, withstand environmental conditions, grow in marginal lands, fix atmospheric nitrogen, enhance soil biodiversity, and more. However, multidimensional factors lead to an abundance of stakeholders and hinder their expansion in agricultural systems [4, 68, 125].

These issues stem from alterations in land use and harvesting practices; agronomical traits and yield; short shelf life; lack of supply systems related to seed dissemination; biotic and abiotic factors that hinder productivity and profitability; changes in dietary patterns led by the fast food industry and culture; negative stereotypes against uncommon food resources; presence of toxic and allergic compounds; lack of knowledge and awareness of the nutritional values of available local varieties; non-popular taste; and loss of indigenous skills for preparing dishes based on these plants. In addition, low commercial value and poor economic competitiveness compared to common cash crops, marketing constraints, and the absence of national policies, strategies, programs, and schemes to promote the introduction of such plants into agricultural systems widely further limit their utilization [2].

6.1 Agronomic challenges

Bambara groundnut (*Vigna subterranea*) grows well in drought and low-input agriculture systems, fixing nitrogen. Nevertheless, its wider adoption is limited by the low yield of 500–1,500 kg ha^{-1}, which is considered low for such an area of land compared to other crops [138]. Grass pea (*Lathyrus sativus* L.) thrives in a wide range of conditions, has a deep root system, and is nutritionally valuable. Yet, it has limitations preventing it from spreading in agrosystems: It yields less, and it contains a neurotoxic compound (ODAP) at 0.1–2.5 g kg^{-1} DM, associated with lathyrism. Mitigation could be achieved by developing low-ODAP cultivars and using proper processing methods such as boiling and soaking, which decrease ODAP by 50–70%, as well as fermentation [123].

Winged bean (*Psophocarpus tetragonolobus*) is adaptable to humid climates, fixing nitrogen, increasing the yield of subsequent crops, and adding to its nutritional value. Despite these advantages, the growth style of this plant hinders its spread in the agricultural system. It takes four to six months to yield only 1,000 to 2000 kg ha^{-1} collected by the workforce [139]. Also, the presence of tannins can cause digestive disorders. Breeding efforts for shorter growth periods and mechanization, in addition to processing methods reducing tannins, shall increase the importance of this crop [124]. Underutilized legumes, such as *Cajanus cajan* (pigeon pea), are traditionally prepared by soaking and boiling for dishes like dhal, but these methods demand extended preparation and cooking times, hindering their scalability for modern markets [125].

Kersting's groundnut (*Macrotyloma geocarpum*) is valued for its high protein content and essential amino acid profile. Still, it yields less than 500 kg ha^{-1}, far below that of common crops. In addition to its self-pollination nature, the genetic base is narrow, constraining the flexibility of breeding for new varieties. Collecting and testing cultivars from different ecologies and using new techniques to overcome the crossability issues would speed up the research pipeline for this crop's expansion [209]. Pod-shattering is a trait in some underutilized legumes that poses a critical challenge: Ripened pods release their seeds on the ground, significantly reducing yield [210].

Some underutilized legumes are costly to produce; thus, if the yield and price are profitable, that could easily prevent their expansion. For example, AYB needs staking, which could be available in some regions and costly in others. Bambara groundnuts are a shrubby plant cultivated mainly by the workforce, found in some regions but rare in others [68].

6.2 Market and consumer barriers

Consumption of legumes varied widely across regions and cultures [68]. In Asia and Africa, people commonly incorporate legumes into their diets. In Western countries, only 20% of adults consume pulses, compared to 80% who prefer meat, mainly due to taste preferences, lengthy preparation time, and digestive issues. Strategies to increase individual knowledge of the nutritional importance and market for new varieties of processed foods shall boost legume acceptance and generate market demand. For example, in Rwanda's schools, providing bean-based meals raised students' legume consumption by 25%, fostering lasting dietary habits [125]. Various processing techniques have been proposed to reduce anti-nutritional factors in legumes, such as water soaking, boiling, simmering, autoclaving, microwave irradiation, hot sand parching, roasting, baking, pounding, acidic/alkaline soaking, and lime treatment [211]. The purpose or proposed use of underutilized legumes should be considered before deciding to reduce their anti-nutrients. For instance, in pharmaceutical applications, these compounds are valuable and should be enhanced, whereas in food applications, reduction is essential to improve safety and digestibility [68].

6.3 Research and institutional gaps

Identification of agronomic traits controlling factors, especially seed-related traits, is considered fundamental for research efforts aimed at developing competitive and resilient plants. In this regard, agronomic and genetic information for such crops is currently limited, and more efforts, such as phenotyping and related research, are required to facilitate progress. The nutritional profiles of seeds are governed by genetic and metabolic pathways; further clarification of any anti-nutritional factors will ease the way for researchers to provide optimal solutions to overcome these challenges.

7. Future prospects and research priorities

Underutilized legumes represent a potential resource for mitigating future challenges of food security and sustainable agriculture. The plant-based protein market is experiencing rapid growth, driven by rising global demand for sustainable dietary resources, with projections reaching up to a 14% annual growth rate by 2027 [125]. Alongside the climate change crisis and population growth pressures, these plants are expected to become increasingly crucial for resilient food systems.

One of the most critical drivers of underutilized legumes is their high potential to contribute to nutritional security. Many of these species provide high-quality protein, dietary fiber, essential minerals, and bioactive compounds. With growing concern about unbalanced diets and malnutrition, the broader adoption of these plants could provide a more balanced, affordable diet, particularly in developing and low-income regions. Future research seeking to address issues related to anti-nutritional factors and nutrient bioavailability will enhance the nutritional value of these foods.

In the agriculture integrative system, underutilized legumes offer resilient solutions. Their adaptability to different marginal ecological conditions, tolerance to drought, survival in extreme temperatures, growth in poor soils, atmospheric nitrogen fixation, lower need for fertilizers, and enhancement of soil biodiversity make them suitable for low-input farming systems. Integration of these crops in agricultural rotation and intercropping systems will enhance agroecosystem sustainability in the future.

Currently available plant breeding and biotechnology tools are expected to play a significant role in unlocking these plants' potential. The collection, conservation, and characterization of germplasm from different locations, combined with modern tools, can accelerate the development of competitive varieties with higher yield, nutritional attributes, and environmental adaptability. Such efforts are essential for increasing their commercial viability and acceptance by farmers.

Food processing technologies present future opportunities. New processing methods for legume-based food products, such as flours, snacks, extruded legume protein products, high-moisture meat analogues (HMMA), and fibrous plant protein products, can improve consumer acceptance, market demand, and economic value. Innovations in this sector can address a significant part of the constraints to the widespread use of underutilized legumes and expand their use beyond local production areas, thereby generating driving forces for their broader integration into agricultural systems.

Although they have potential, qualifying them for greater integration in agricultural systems, widespread adoption requires the coordination of multidisciplinary efforts. Prospects aiming at new policy frameworks, market development, and increased awareness can help create value chains and further integrate these potential plants into agricultural systems.

In conclusion, underutilized legumes hold substantial potential for sustainable food and agriculture, yet this potential remains largely underexploited. With synchronized efforts in research, breeding, processing, policy frameworks, and market integration, these legumes could play a crucial role in bridging the food gap in the years to come.

Conflict of Interest

The authors declare no conflict of interest.

Author details

Mohamed A. S. Khalifa[1*], Asmaa H. Zaki[2], Ali Hassan Anany[3] and Bahaa Abugammie[4]

1 Department of Ornamental Horticulture, Faculty of Agriculture, Cairo University, Giza, Egypt

2 Department of Agricultural Chemistry, Faculty of Agriculture, Minia University, Minya, Egypt

3 Egyptian National Gene Bank, Agricultural Research Center, Giza, Egypt

4 Department of Genetics, Faculty of Agriculture, Minia University, Minya, Egypt

*Address all correspondence to: Mohamed.said@agr.cu.edu.eg

References

[1] Khan MMH, Rafii MY, Ramlee SI, Jusoh M, Al-Mamun M. Bambara groundnut (*Vigna subterranea* L. Verdc.): A crop for the new millennium, its genetic diversity, and improvements to mitigate future food and nutritional challenges. Sustainability. 2021;**13**(10):1–27

[2] Knez M, Ranić M, Gurinović M. Underutilized plants increase biodiversity, improve food and nutrition security, reduce malnutrition, and enhance human health and well-being. Let's put them back on the plate! Nutrition Reviews. 2024;**82**(8):1111–1124

[3] Majola NG. Breeding Bambara Groundnut (*Vigna subterranea* (L.) Verdc) for Enhanced Yield and Nutritional Quality in South Africa. Pietermaritzburg: University of Kwazulu-Natal; 2023. Available from: https://researchspace.ukzn.ac.za/items/7bebe189-775e-489d-94fe-e5c4ae1f137a [Accessed: 2026-February-23]

[4] Cullis C, Kunert KJ. Unlocking the potential of orphan legumes. Journal of Experimental Botany. 2017;**68**(8):1895–1903

[5] Balestrazzi A, Calvio C, Macovei A, Pagano A, Laux P, Moutahir H, et al. Seed quality as a proxy of climate-ready orphan legumes: The need for a multidisciplinary and multi-actor vision. Frontiers in Plant Science. 2024;**15**(August):1–12

[6] Smýkal P, Coyne CJ, Ambrose MJ, Maxted N, Schaefer H, Blair MW, et al. Legume crops phylogeny and genetic diversity for science and breeding. Critical Reviews in Plant Sciences. 2015;**34**:43–104

[7] Smýkal P, Kenicer G, Flavell AJ, Corander J, Kosterin O, Redden RJ, et al. Phylogeny, phylogeography and genetic diversity of the Pisum genus. Plant Genetic Resources. 2011;**9**:4–18

[8] Lewis GP, Schrire B, Mackinder B, Lock M, (eds). Legumes of the World. Vol. Richmond, UK. Royal Botanic Gardens Kew; 2005. p. 577

[9] FAO. The Third Report on the State of the World's Plant Genetic Resources for Food and Agriculture [Internet]. Rome, Italy: FAO Commission on Genetic Resources for Food and Agriculture Assessments; 2025. Available from: https://www.fao.org/family-farming/detail/en/c/1741574/[[Accessed: 2025-October-21]

[10] Frankel OH, Brown AHD, Holden JHW, Williams JT. Crop Genetic Resources: Conservation and Evaluation. Lodon: George Allen and Unwin; 1984

[11] Khoury C, Laliberté B, Guarino L. Trends in ex situ conservation of plant genetic resources: A review of global crop and regional conservation strategies. Genetic Resources and Crop Evolution. 2010;**57**(4):625–639

[12] Snook LK, Dulloo ME, Jarvis A, Scheldeman X, Kneller M. Crop germplasm diversity: The role of gene bank collections in facilitating adaptation to climate change. Crop Adaptation to Climate Change. Wallingford, UK CABI; 2011. 345–360

[13] Bao S, He Y, Zong X, Wang L, Li L, Enneking D, et al Collection of pea ("*Pisum sativum*") and faba bean ("*Vicia faba*") germplasm in Yunnan. Plant

Genetic Resources Newsletter= Bulletin de Ressources Phytogénétiques= Noticiario de Recursos Fitogenéticos. 2008;**156**:11–22

[14] Hui LY, Zhang C, Smulders MJM, Li W, song MY, Xu Q, et al. Analysis of average standardized SSR allele size supports domestication of soybean along the Yellow River. Genetic Resources and Crop Evolution. 2013;**60**:763–776

[15] Li X, Acharya A, Farmer AD, Crow JA, Bharti AK, Kramer RS, et al. Prevalence of single nucleotide polymorphism among 27 diverse alfalfa genotypes as assessed by transcriptome sequencing. BMC Genomics. 2012;**13**:568

[16] Heywood VH. The role of botanic gardens as resource and introduction centres in the face of global change. Biodiversity and Conservation. 2011;**20** (2):221–239

[17] Ramírez-Villegas J, Khoury C, Jarvis A, Debouck DG, Guarino L. A gap analysis methodology for collecting crop genepools: A case study with *Phaseolus* beans. PLoS One. 2010;**5**(10): e13497

[18] Shehadeh A, Amri A, Maxted N. Ecogeographic survey and gap analysis of *Lathyrus* L. species. Genetic Resources and Crop Evolution. 2013;**60** (7):2101–2113

[19] Ford-Lloyd B, Maxted N, Hawkes JG. Plant Genetic Conservation: The in Situ Approach. London; New York: Chapman & Hall; 1997. p. 446. DOI: 10.1007/978-94-009-1437-7

[20] Maxted N, Bennett SJ. Plant Genetic Resources of Legumes in the Mediterranean. Dordrecht, Netherlands. Springer Science & Business Media; 2001. p. 386

[21] Maxted N. An ecogeographical study of Vicia subgenus Vicia. 1995

[22] Engels JMM, Rao VR, Brown AHD, Jackson MT. Managing plant genetic diversity. (eds.). Managing Plant Genetic Diversity. Wallingford, UK: CABI. 2001. p. 520

[23] Nusret Z, Kaya Z, Anikster Y, Adams WT. The Proceedings of International Symposium on in situ conservation of Plant Genetic Diversity. 1998

[24] Amri A, Monzer M, Al-Oqla A, Atawneh N, Shehadeh A, Konopka J. Status and treats to natural habitats and crop wild relatives in selected areas in West Asia region. In: Proceedings of the International Conference on promoting community-driven in situ conservation of dryland agrobiodiversity; Aleppo, Syria: ICARDA; 2008

[25] Amri A, Ajlouni M, Assi R, Sbeih Y, Saad A, Khoury W, et al. Major achievements of the West Asia Dryland agrobiodiversity conservation project. In: Proceedings of the International Conference on promoting community-driven in situ conservation of dryland agrobiodiversity; Aleppo, Syria: ICARDA; 2008

[26] Maxted N, Kell SP, Ford-Lloyd BV. Crop wild relative conservation and use: Establishing the context. In: Crop Wild Relative Conservation and Use. Wallingford, UK: CABI; 2007. p. 3–30

[27] Schaefer H, Hechenleitner P, Santos-Guerra A, de Sequeira MM, Pennington RT, Kenicer G, et al. Systematics, biogeography, and character evolution of the legume tribe

Fabeae with special focus on the middle-Atlantic island lineages. BMC Evolutionary Biology. 2012;**12**:250

[28] Steele KP, Wojciechowski M, Klitgaard B, Bruneau A. Phylogenetic analyses of tribes Trifolieae and Vicieae, based on sequences of the plastid gene matK (Papilionoideae: Leguminosae). In: Advances in Legume Systematics Part 10: Higher Level Systematics. London, UK: Royal Botanic Gardens, Kew; 2003. p. 355–370

[29] Lavin M, A DS. Pollen brush of Papilionoideae (Leguminosae): Morphological variation and systematic utility. American Journal of Botany. 1990;**77**(10):1294–1312

[30] Kenicer GJ, Kajita T, Pennington RT, Murata J. Systematics and biogeography of *Lathyrus* (Leguminosae) based on internal transcribed spacer and cpDNA sequence data. American Journal of Botany. 2005;**92**(7):1199–1209

[31] Patto MCV, Skiba B, Pang ECK, Ochatt SJ, Lambein F, Rubiales D. *Lathyrus* improvement for resistance against biotic and abiotic stresses: From classical breeding to marker assisted selection. Euphytica. 2006;**147**(1):133–147

[32] Ladizinsky G. The origin of lentil and its wild genepool. Euphytica. 1979;**28**(1):179–187

[33] FERGUSON ME, Maxted N, Van Slageren M, Robertson LD. A re-assessment of the taxonomy of *Lens* Mill.(Leguminosae, Papilionoideae, Vicieae). Botanical Journal of the Linnean Society. 2000;**133**(1):41–59

[34] V TA, Gorshkov AP, Kimeklis AK, Onishchuk OP, Vorobiev MG, Andronov EE, et al. Morphology of *Vavilovia formosa* (Steven) Fed. Nodules Induced by Different Rhizobia Strains. Plants. 2025;**14**(24). https://www.mdpi.com/2223-7747/14/24/3764

[35] Maureira-Butler IJ, Pfeil BE, Muangprom A, Osborn TC, Doyle JJ. The reticulate history of *Medicago* (Fabaceae). Systematic Biology. 2008;**57**(3):466–482

[36] Polhill RM, Raven PH, (eds.). Advances in Legume Systematics, Part 1. Kew, UK. Royal Botanic Gardens; 1981. p. 852

[37] Small E Alfalfa and relatives: Evolution and classification of Medicago [Internet]. Ottawa, Canada: NRC research press; 2011. Available from: https://agris.fao.org/search/en/records/65de12cd0f3e94b9e5ca6b07 [Accessed: 2026-February-23]

[38] Ladizinsky G, Adler A. Genetic relationships among the annual species of *Cicer* L. Theoretical and Applied Genetics. 1976;**48**(4):197–203

[39] Toker C. A note on the evolution of kabuli chickpeas as shown by induced mutations in *Cicer reticulatum* Ladizinsky. Genetic Resources and Crop Evolution. 2009;**56**(1):7–12

[40] Varshney RK, Song C, Saxena RK, Azam S, Yu S, Sharpe AG, et al. Draft genome sequence of chickpea (*Cicer arietinum*) provides a resource for trait improvement. Nat Biotechnol. 2013;**31**:240–246

[41] Freytag GF, Debouck DG Taxonomy, distribution, and ecology of the genus *Phaseolus* (Leguminosae–Papilionoideae) in North America [Internet]. Mexico and Central America. Texas (TX), USA: Fort

Worth, Botanical Research Institute of Texas; 2002. Available from: https://agris.fao.org/search/en/records/65ddd5f30f3e94b9e5c5a292 [Accessed: 2026-February-23]

[42] Delgado-Salinas A, Turley T, Richman A, Lavin M. Phylogenetic analysis of the cultivated and wild species of *Phaseolus* (Fabaceae). Systematic Botany. 1999;**24** (3):438–460. DOI: 10.2307/2419699

[43] Vaillancourt RE, Weeden NF, Bruneau A, Doyle JJ. Chloroplast DNA phylogeny of old world *Vigna* (Leguminosae). Systematic Botany. 1993. p. 642–651. DOI: 10.2307/2419538

[44] Tomooka N, Vaughan DA, Moss H, Maxted N (eds.). The Asian *Vigna*. Genus *Vigna* Subgenus *Ceratotropis* Genetic Resources. Dordrecht, The Netherlands: Kluwer Academic Publishers; 2002. p. 285

[45] Kim MY, Lee S, Van K, Kim TH, Jeong SC, Choi IY, et al. Whole-genome sequencing and intensive analysis of the undomesticated soybean (*Glycine soja* Sieb. and Zucc.) genome. Proceedings of the National Academy of Sciences. 2010;**107**:22032–22037

[46] Li L, Redden RJ, Zong X, Berger JD, Bennett SJ. Ecogeographic analysis of pea collection sites from China to determine potential sites with abiotic stresses. Genetic Resources and Crop Evolution. 2013;**60** (6):1801–1815

[47] Jimenez-Lopez JC, Singh KB, Clemente A, Czubinski J, Ochatt S, Von Wettberg E *et al*. Editorial: Legumes for global food security - volume II. Frontiers in Plant Science. 2023;**14**: 1273600. DOI: 10.3389/fpls.2023.1273600

[48] Maphosa Y, Jideani VA. The role of legumes in human nutrition. Functional Food-Improve Health Through Adequate Food. 2017;**1**:13

[49] Vadivel V, Patel A, Biesalski HK. Effect of traditional processing methods on the antioxidant, α-amylase and α-glucosidase enzyme inhibition properties of Sesbania sesban Merrill seeds. CyTA-Journal of Food. 2012;**10** (2):128–136

[50] Barman AM, Marak C, Mitra Barman R, Sangma C. Nutraceutical Properties of Legume Seeds and Their Impact on Human Health [Internet]. Legume Seed Nutraceutical Research. IntechOpen; 2019. DOI: 10.5772/intechopen.78799

[51] Cheng A, Raai MN, Zain NAM, Massawe F, Singh A, Waaqi W-M. In search of alternative proteins: Unlocking the potential of underutilized tropical legumes. Food Security. 2019;**11** (6):1205–1215

[52] Cheng A. Shaping a sustainable food future by rediscovering long-forgotten ancient grains. Plant Science. 2018;**269**:136–142

[53] Soetan KO. Preliminary studies on the nutritional and antinutritional constituents of six accessions of African Yam Bean (Sphenostylis stenocarpa), an underutilized legume. Journal of Applied Research on Children. 2017;**8** (2):625 https://openurl.ebsco.com/EPDB%3Agcd%3A3%3A33762067/detailv2?sid=ebsco%3Aplink%3Acrawler-gcd&id=ebsco%3Agcd%3A128352865&crl=f&jrnl=21555834&link_origin=scholar.google.com.eg

[54] Vadivel V, Janardhanan K. Chemical composition of the underutilized legume *Cassia hirsuta* L.

Plant Foods for Human Nutrition. 2000;**55**(4):369–381

[55] K VV. J. Nutritional and anti-nutritional composition of velvet bean: An under-utilized food legume in South India. International Journal of Food Science and Nutrition. 2000;**51** (4):279–287

[56] Ibirinde DO, Aremu CO, Balogun K, Oladokun L. Assessment of seed and tuber production potential in varieties of *Sphenostylis stenocarpa* (Africa Yam Bean). Agricultural Sciences. 2019;**10**:870–881

[57] Oyedele TA, Kehinde IA, Oyelakin AS, Popoola TOS, Atanda HY, Mur LAJ. Identifying the fungal diseases of African Yam Bean (*Sphenostylis stenocarpa*) and their incidence in south-west Nigeria. Physiological and Molecular Plant Pathology. 2024;**130**:106234

[58] Aasim M, Baloch FS, Nadeem MA, Bakhsh A, Sameeullah M, Day S. Fenugreek (*Trigonella foenum-graecum* L.): An underutilized edible plant of modern world . In: Global Perspectives on Underutilized Crops Cham, Switzerland: Springer; 2018. p. 381–408

[59] Jain D, Kumari A, Saheewala H, Sanadhya S, Maheshwari D, Meena RH, et al. Biochemical, functional and molecular characterization of pigeon pea rhizobia isolated from semi-arid regions of India. Archives of Microbiology. 2020;**202**(7):1809–1816. DOI: 10.1007/s00203-020-01904-0

[60] Ndagijimana S, Kabano I, Ntaganda JM. Analysis of risk factors that influence stunting among Rwandan children under the age of five. African Journal of Food, Agriculture, Nutrition and Development. 2022;**22**(5):20480–20497

[61] Correia MITD, Tappenden KA, Malone A, Prado CM, Evans DC, Sauer AC, et al. Utilization and validation of the Global Leadership Initiative on Malnutrition (GLIM): A scoping review. Clinical Nutrition. 2022;**41**:687–697

[62] Brown DL. Canavanine-induced longevity in mice may require diets with greater than 15.7% protein. Nutrition and Metabolism (London). 2005;**2**(1):7

[63] Baiyeri SO, Uguru MI, Ogbonna PE, Samuel-Baiyeri CCA, Okechukwu R, Kumaga FK, et al. Evaluation of the nutritional composition of the seeds of some selected African yam bean (*Sphenostylis stenocarpa* Hochst Ex. A. Rich (Harms)) Accessions. Agro-Science. 2018;**17**:37–44

[64] CV N, Ajayi SA, Oselebe HO, Atkinson CJ, Adewale DB, Igwe DO, et al. Updates on nutritional diversity in Sphenostylis stenocarpa (Hoechst ex. A. Rich.) harms. For food security and conservation. American Journal of Agricultural and Biological Sciences. 2018;**13**:38–49

[65] Adedayo BC, Anyasi TA, Taylor MJC, Rautenbauch F, Le Roes-Hill M, Jideani VA. Phytochemical composition and antioxidant properties of methanolic extracts of whole and dehulled Bambara groundnut (*Vigna subterranea*) seeds. Scientific Reports. 2021;**11**(1):14116

[66] Adegboyega TT, Abberton MT, Abdelgadir AH, Dianda M, Maziya-Dixon B, Oyatomi OA, et al. Nutrient and Antinutrient Composition of Winged Bean (*Psophocarpus*

tetragonolobus (L.) DC.) Seeds and Tubers. Journal of Food Quality. 2019;**2019**:3075208

[67] Semba RD, Ramsing R, Rahman N, Kraemer K, Bloem MW. Legumes as a sustainable source of protein in human diets. Global Food Security. 2021;**28**:100520

[68] Ayilara MS, Abberton M, Oyatomi OA, Odeyemi O, Babalola OO Potentials of underutilized legumes in food security. 2022:1–12

[69] Bessada SMF, Barreira JCM, Oliveira MBPP. Pulses and food security: Dietary protein, digestibility, bioactive and functional properties. Trends in Food Science and Technology. 2019;**93**:53–68

[70] Tan XL, Azam-Ali S, Von GE, Mustafa M, Chai HH, Ho WK, et al. Bambara Groundnut: An Underutilized Leguminous Crop for Global Food Security and Nutrition. Frontiers in Nutrition. 2020;**7**:601496

[71] James S, Nwabueze TU, Ndife J, Onwuka GI, Usman MA, Audu Y. Effects of treatments on some bioactive components of selected lesser known legumes indigenous to Nigeria. Journal of Food Chemistry and Nanotechnology. 2020;**6**(4):197–206

[72] Cui H, Abdel-Samie MAS, Lin L, Jafari SM. Application of antimicrobial-loaded nano/microcarriers in different food products. In: Application of Nano/ Microencapsulated Ingredients in Food Products Amsterdam, Netherlands: Elsevier; 2021. p. 469–517

[73] Zheng Z, Li J, Li J, Sun H, Liu Y. Physicochemical and antioxidative characteristics of black bean protein hydrolysates obtained from different enzymes. Food Hydrocolloids. 2019;**97**:105222

[74] Shevkani K, Singh N, Patil C, Awasthi A, Paul M. Antioxidative and antimicrobial properties of pulse proteins and their applications in gluten-free foods and sports nutrition. International Journal of Food Science and Technology. 2022;**57** (9):5571–5584

[75] Oboh G, Agunloye OM, Adefegha SA, Akinyemi AJ, Ademiluyi AO. Caffeic and chlorogenic acids inhibit key enzymes linked to type 2 diabetes (in vitro): A comparative study. Journal of Basic and Clinical Physiology and Pharmacology. 2015;**26** (2):165–170

[76] Soetan KO, Adeola AA. Comparative nutritional and functional properties of selected underutilized legumes. Nigerian Journal of Animal Production. 2018;**45**(3):96–106

[77] Ikhajiagbe B, Ogwu MC, Ogochukwu OF, Odozi EB, Adekunle IJ, Omage ZE. The place of neglected and underutilized legumes in human nutrition and protein security in Nigeria. Critical Reviews in Food Science and Nutrition. 2022;**62** (14):3930–3938

[78] Amarowicz R, Pegg RB. Legumes as a source of natural antioxidants. European Journal of Lipid Science and Technology. 2008;**110**(10):865–878

[79] Alcázar-Valle M, Lugo-Cervantes E, Mojica L, Morales-Hernández N, Reyes-Ramírez H, Enríquez-Vara JN, et al. Bioactive compounds, antioxidant activity, and antinutritional content of legumes: A comparison between four Phaseolus species. Molecules. 2020;**25**:3528

[80] Bhadkaria A, Srivastava N, Bhagyawant SS. A prospective of underutilized legume moth bean (*Vigna aconitifolia* (Jacq.) Marechàl): Phytochemical profiling, bioactive compounds and in vitro pharmacological studies. Food Bioscience. 2021;**42**:101088

[81] Yang CS, Landau JM, Huang MT, Newmark HL. Inhibition of carcinogenesis by dietary polyphenolic compounds. Annual Review of Nutrition. 2001;**21**(1):381–406

[82] Okafor JNC, Jideani VA, Meyer M, Le Roes-Hill M. Bioactive components in Bambara groundnut (*Vigna subterranea* (L.) Verdc) as a potential source of nutraceutical ingredients. Heliyon. 2022;**8**(3):e09024

[83] Ade-Omowaye BIO, Tucker GA, Smetanska I. Nutritional potential of nine underexploited legumes in Southwest Nigeria. International Food Research Journal. 2015;**22**(2):798

[84] Nadeem MA, Karaköy T, Yeken MZ, Habyarimana E, Hatipoğlu R, Çiftçi V, et al. Phenotypic characterization of 183 Turkish common bean accessions for agronomic, trading, and consumer-preferred plant characteristics for breeding purposes. Agronomy. 2020;**10**:272

[85] Soetan KO, Olaiya CO, Karigidi KO. Comparative in vitro antioxidant activities of six accessions of African Yam Beans (*Sphenostylis stenocarpa* L.). Annals: Food Science & Technology. 2018;**19**(3):454–466

[86] Harris T, Jideani V, Le Roes-Hill M. Flavonoids and tannin composition of Bambara groundnut (*Vigna subterranea*) of Mpumalanga, South Africa. Heliyon. 2018;**4**(9):e00833

[87] Olaleye AA, Adeyeye EI, Adesina AJ. Chemical composition of bambara groundnut (*V. subterranea* L. Verdc) seed parts. Bangladesh Journal of Scientific and Industrial Research. 2013;**48**(3):167–178

[88] Sreerama YN, Sashikala VB, Pratape VM. Variability in the distribution of phenolic compounds in milled fractions of chickpea and horse gram: Evaluation of their antioxidant properties. Journal of Agricultural and Food Chemistry. 2010;**58**(14):8322–8330

[89] Bhagyawant SS, Bhadkaria A, Narvekar DT, Srivastava N. Multivariate biochemical characterization of rice bean (*Vigna umbellata*) seeds for nutritional enhancement. Biocatalysis and Agricultural Biotechnology. 2019;**20**:101193

[90] Yao Y, Cheng XZ, Wang LX, Wang SH, Ren G. Major phenolic compounds, antioxidant capacity and antidiabetic potential of rice bean (*Vigna umbellata* L.) in China. International Journal of Molecular Sciences. 2012;**13**(3):2707–2716

[91] Kaur D, Rasane P, Dhawan K, Singh J, Kaur S, Gurumayum S, et al. Rice bean (*Vigna umbellata*) based ready-to-eat geriatric premix: Optimization and analysis. Journal of Food Processing and Preservation 2021;**45**:e16075

[92] Rao S, Chinkwo KA, Santhakumar AB, Blanchard CL. Inhibitory effects of pulse bioactive compounds on cancer development pathways. Diseases. 2018;**6**(3):72

[93] Sai D, Nagaraju R, Kamalakar PP. Nutritional potentiality of an Underutilized Food legume: Lima bean.

Journal of Emerging Technologies and Innovative Research. 2024;**11**(7):530–540

[94] da S A-CT, Teodoro AFP, de B Das N AR, Braga LR, Ribeiro IF, Silva JP, et al. Fenólicos, flavonoides, taninos totais e atividade antioxidante de fava conservada em banco de germoplasma. Ciência Rural. 2015;**45**:335–341

[95] Drago SR, Franco-Miranda H, Cian RE, Betancur-Ancona D, Chel-Guerrero L. Bioactive properties of *Phaseolus lunatus* (Lima Bean) and *Vigna unguiculata* (Cowpea) hydrolyzates incorporated into pasta. Residual activity after pasta cooking. Plant Foods for Human Nutrition. 2016;**71**(3):339–345

[96] Fasoyiro SB, Ajibade SR, Omole AJ, Adeniyan ON, Farinde EO. Proximate, minerals and antinutritional factors of some underutilized grain legumes in south-western Nigeria. Nutrition & Food Science. 2006;**36**(1):18–23

[97] Chhikara N, Devi HR, Jaglan S, Sharma P, Gupta P, Panghal A. Bioactive compounds, food applications and health benefits of *Parkia speciosa* (stinky beans): A review. Agriculture & Food Security. 2018;**7**(1):1–9

[98] Basu S, Ghosh M, Bhunia RK, Ganguly J, Banik BK. Polysaccharides from *Dolichos biflorus* Linn and *Trachyspermum ammi* Linn seeds: Isolation, characterization and remarkable antimicrobial activity. Chemistry Central Journal. 2017;**11**(1):118

[99] Johnson JB, Neupane P, Bhattarai SP, Trotter T, Naiker M. Partitioning of nutritional and phytochemical constituents in nine Adzuki bean genotypes from Australia. Journal of Agricultural and Food Research. 2022;**10**:100398

[100] Luo J, Cai W, Wu T, Xu B. Phytochemical distribution in hull and cotyledon of adzuki bean (*Vigna angularis* L.) and mung bean (*Vigna radiate* L.), and their contribution to antioxidant, anti-inflammatory and anti-diabetic activities. Food Chemistry. 2016;**201**:350–360

[101] Ko HJ, Ang LH, Ng LT. Antioxidant Activities and Polyphenolic Constituents of Bitter Bean *Parkia Speciosa*. International Journal of Food Properties. 2014;**17**(9):1977–1986

[102] Jamaluddin F, Mohamed S, Lajis MN. Hypoglycaemic effect of *Parkia speciosa* seeds due to the synergistic action of β-sitosterol and stigmasterol. Food Chemistry. 1994;**49**(4):339–345

[103] Ojuederie OB, Balogun MO, Abberton MT. Mechanism for pollination in African yam bean. African Crop Science Journal. 2016;**24**(4):405–416

[104] George TT, Obilana AO, Oyeyinka SA. The prospects of African yam bean: Past and future importance. Heliyon. 2020;**6**(11):e05458

[105] Huang J, Yang Q, Pu H. Slowly digestible starch. In: Functional Starch and Applications in Food. Singapore: Springer; 2018. p. 27–61

[106] Chandrasekara A, Josheph Kumar T. Roots and tuber crops as functional foods: A review on phytochemical constituents and their potential health benefits. International Journal of Food Science. 2016;**2016**(1):3631647

[107] Divekar PA, Narayana S, Divekar BA, Kumar R, Gadratagi BG,

Ray A, et al. Plant secondary metabolites as defense tools against herbivores for sustainable crop protection. International Journal of Molecular Sciences. 2022;**23**:2690

[108] Kahane R, Hodgkin T, Jaenicke H, Hoogendoorn C, Hermann M, Keatinge JDH, et al. Agrobiodiversity for food security, health and income. Agronomy for Sustainable Development. 2013;**33**:671–693

[109] Lamien N, Lingani-Coulibaly P, Traore-Gue J. Importance of local fruits consumption in diet balance in Burkina Faso, West Africa. In: International Symposium on Underutilized Plants for Food Security, Nutrition, Income and Sustainable Development 806. 2008. p. 203–208

[110] Jenkins DJA, Kendall CWC, Augustin LSA, Mitchell S, Sahye-Pudaruth S, Mejia SB, et al. Effect of legumes as part of a low glycemic index diet on glycemic control and cardiovascular risk factors in type 2 diabetes mellitus: A randomized controlled trial. Archives of Internal Medicine. 2012;**172**:1653–1660

[111] Becerra-Tomás N, Díaz-López A, Rosique-Esteban N, Ros E, Buil-Cosiales P, Corella D, et al. Legume consumption is inversely associated with type 2 diabetes incidence in adults: A prospective assessment from the PREDIMED study. Clinical Nutrition. 2018;**37**:906–913

[112] Bazzano LA, Thompson AM, Tees MT, Nguyen CH, Winham DM. Non-soy legume consumption lowers cholesterol levels: A meta-analysis of randomized controlled trials. Nutrition, Metabolism and Cardiovascular Diseases. 2011;**21**(2):94–103

[113] Jayalath VH, De Souza RJ, Sievenpiper JL, Ha V, Chiavaroli L, Mirrahimi A, et al. Effect of dietary pulses on blood pressure: A systematic review and meta-analysis of controlled feeding trials. American Journal of Hypertension. 2014;**27**:56–64

[114] Wang Y, Wang Z, Fu L, Chen Y, Fang J. Legume consumption and colorectal adenoma risk: A meta-analysis of observational studies. PLoS One. 2013;**8**(6):e67335

[115] Li J, Mao QQ. Legume intake and risk of prostate cancer: A meta-analysis of prospective cohort studies. Oncotarget. 2017;**8**(27):44776

[116] Gnankambary K, J. Batieno TB, Dieni Z, Sawadogo P, Thiombiano C, Sawadogo N, et al. Genetic characterization and participatory selection of Kersting's groundnut (*Macrotyloma geocarpum* (Harms)) cultivars for agronomic performance in their producing Zone in Burkina Faso. Journal of Experimental Biology and Agricultural Sciences. 2025;**13**:572–582

[117] Kadhri T, Singh S, Shreya M, Kumar A, Ali SA. Effect of foliar application of nutrients on growth and yield of chickpea. International Journal of Research in Agronomy. 2024;**7**(8S):495–499

[118] Azam-Ali SN, Sesay A, Karikari SK, Massawe FJ, Aguilar-Manjarrez J, Bannayan M, et al. Assessing the potential of an underutilized crop - A case study using bambara groundnut. Experimental Agriculture. 2001;**37**:433–472

[119] Maphosa Y, Jideani VA, Maphosa L. Bambara groundnut production, grain composition and nutritional value: Opportunities

for improvements. Journal of Agricultural Science. 2022;**160** (6):448–458

[120] Ojuederie OB, Akpojotor UL, Adeniji AA, Ojuederie TC, Popoola JO, Babalola OO. Comparative genomic analysis of underutilized legumes: Insights into evolutionary relationships, genome evolution and stress tolerance. Biotechnology Reports. 2025;**48**:e00918. DOI: 10.1016/j.btre.2025.e00918

[121] Rani J, Dhull SB, Kinabo J, Kidwai MK, Sangwan A. A narrative review on nutritional and health benefits of underutilized summer crop to address agriculture challenges: Moth bean (*Vigna aconitifolia* L.). Legume Science. 2023;**5**(4):1–13

[122] Nie J, Harrison MT, Zhou J, Yang L, Zhao J, Wang X, et al. Productivity and water use efficiency of summer soybean-winter wheat rotation system under limited water supply in the North China Plain. European Journal of Agronomy. 2023;**151**:126959. https://www.sciencedirect.com/science/article/abs/pii/S1161030123002277

[123] Das A, Parihar AK, Barpete S, Kumar S, Gupta S. Current Perspectives on Reducing the β-ODAP Content and Improving Potential Agronomic Traits in Grass Pea (*Lathyrus sativus* L.). Frontiers in Plant Science. 2021;**12**:2021. DOI: 10.3389/fpls.2021.703275

[124] Amoah I, Ascione A, Muthanna FMS, Feraco A, Camajani E, Gorini S, et al. Sustainable Strategies for Increasing Legume Consumption: Culinary and Educational Approaches. Foods. 2023;**12**(11):2265. https://www.mdpi.com/2304-8158/12/11/2265

[125] Acheampong R, Osei Tutu C, Owusu-Bempah J, Kumador DK, Mahama S, Kortei NK, et al. Underutilised legumes in regenerative agriculture: Implications for food and nutritional security – A review. Applied Food Research. 2025;**5**(2):101313. DOI: 10.1016/j.afres.2025.101313

[126] Ahmad M, Zahir ZA, Nazli F, Akram F, Arshad M, Khalid M. Effectiveness of halo-tolerant, auxin producing *Pseudomonas* and *Rhizobium* strains to improve osmotic stress tolerance in mung bean (*Vigna radiata* L.). Brazilian Journal of Microbiology. 2013;**44**:1341–1348

[127] Degefu T, Wolde-meskel E, Adem M, Fikre A, Amede T, Ojiewo CO. Morphophysiological diversity of rhizobia nodulating pigeon pea (*Cajanus cajan* L. Millsp.) growing in Ethiopia. African Journal of Biotechnology. 2018;**17**(6):167–177

[128] Fukai S, Hammer GL, et.al. Growth and yield response of barley and chickpea to water stress under three environments in southeast Queensland. II. Root growth and soil water extraction pattern. Australian Journal of Agricultural Research. 1995;**46**:35–48

[129] Mohamed MF, Keutgen N, Tawfika AA, Noga G. Dehydration-avoidance responses of tepary bean lines differing in drought resistance. Journal of Plant Physiology. 2002;**159** (1):31–38

[130] Travlos IS, Karamanos AJ Growth responses of marama bean (Tylosema esculentum) to water deficit conditions. 2008;**3**:155–60

[131] Kong H, Palta JA, Siddique KHM, Stefanova K, Xiong YC, Turner NC. Photosynthesis is Reduced, and Seeds Fail to Set and Fill at Similar Soil Water Contents in Grass Pea (*Lathyrus sativus*

L.) Subjected to Terminal Drought. Journal of Agronomy and Crop Science. 2015;**201**(4):241–252

[132] Gusmao M. Grass pea (*Lathyrus sativus* cv. Ceora): Adaptation to water deficit and benefit in crop rotation [Internet] [Doctor of Philosophy]. [Perth (Australia)]: University of Western Australia; 2010. Available from: https://research-repository.uwa.edu.au/en/publications/grass-pea-lathyrus-sativus-cv-ceora-adaptation-to-water-deficit-a/ [Accessed: 2026-February-23]

[133] Bamshaiye OM, Adegbola JA, Bamishaiye EI. Bambara groundnut: An under-utilized nut in Africa. Advances in Agricultural Biotechnology. 2011;**1** (1):60–72

[134] Charles OO. Sensory Properties of Extruded Meat Analogue from Bambara Groundnut Flour at High Moisture Contents. Department of Food Science and Technology, College of Food Science and Human Ecology. Abeokuta, Nigeria: College of Food Science and Human Ecology, University of Agriculture; 2010

[135] FAO. Key messages :Global Symposium on Soil Erosion (GSER19). 2019. Available from: https://www.fao.org/about/meetings/soil-erosion-symposium/key-messages/en/?utm_source=chatgpt.com [Accessed: 2026-February-23]

[136] Drinkwater LE, Snapp SS. Advancing the science and practice of ecological nutrient management for smallholder farmers. Frontiers in Sustainable Food Systems. 2022;**6**:921216

[137] Mayes S, Ho WK, Chai HH, Gao X, Kundy AC, Mateva KI, et al. Bambara groundnut: An exemplar underutilised legume for resilience under climate change. Planta. 2019;**250**:803–820

[138] Beebe SE, Rao IM, Devi MJ, Polania J. Common beans, biodiversity, and multiple stresses: Challenges of drought resistance in tropical soils. Crop & Pasture Science. 2014;**65**(7):667–675

[139] Sriwichai S, Monkham T, Sanitchon J, Jogloy S, Chankaew S. Dual-purpose of the winged bean (*Psophocarpus tetragonolobus* (L.) DC.), the neglected Tropical legume, based on pod and tuber yields. Plants. 2021;**10** (8):1746

[140] Samal I, Bhoi TK, Raj MN, Majhi PK, Murmu S, Pradhan AK Underutilized legumes : Nutrient status and advanced breeding approaches for qualitative and quantitative enhancement. 2023

[141] Gonçalves L, Rubiales D, Bronze MR, Vaz Patto MC. Grass Pea (Lathyrus sativus L.) –A Sustainable and Resilient Answer to Climate Challenges. Agronomy. 2022;**12**(6):1324. DOI: 10.3390/agronomy12061324

[142] Majola NG, Gerrano AS, Shimelis H. Bambara groundnut (*Vigna subterranea* [L.] Verdc.) production, utilisation and genetic improvement in Sub-Saharan Africa. Agronomy. 2021; **11**(7):1345

[143] Carranca C, Torres MO, Madeira M. Underestimated role of legume roots for soil N fertility. Agronomy for Sustainable Development. 2015;**35**(3):1095–1102

[144] Thilakarathna MS, McElroy MS, Chapagain T, Papadopoulos YA, Raizada MN. Belowground nitrogen

transfer from legumes to non-legumes under managed herbaceous cropping systems. A review. Agronomy for Sustainable Development. 2016;**36**(4):58

[145] Uher D, Svečnjak Z, Dujmović-Purgar D, Jareš D, Horvatić I. Influence of intercropping maize with climbing bean on forage yield and quality. Agroforestry International Journal. 2019;**4**(3):60–67

[146] Adjei-Nsiah S. Role of pigeonpea cultivation on soil fertility and farming system sustainability in Ghana. International Journal of Agronomy. 2012;**2012**(1):702506

[147] Babalola OO, Olanrewaju OS, Dias T, Ajilogba CF, Kutu FR, Cruz C. Biological nitrogen fixation: The role of underutilized leguminous plants. In: Microorganisms for Green Revolution: Volume 1: Microbes for Sustainable Crop Production. Singapore: Springer; 2017. p. 431–443

[148] Nahunnaro H, Bayaso I. Inhibitory activity of plant extracts on the early blight pathogen *Aalternaria solani*. Global Journal of Agricultural Sciences. 2012;**11**(1):57–62

[149] Lu Y, Chen Q, Bu Y, Luo R, Hao S, Zhang J, et al Flavonoid accumulation plays an important role in the rust resistance of *Malus* plant leaves. Frontiers in Plant Science. 2017;**8**:1286

[150] V RS, Pal R, Vaiphei K, Sharma SK, Ola RP. Garlic in health and disease. Nutrition Research Reviews. 2011;**24**(1):60–71

[151] Were E, Schöne J, Viljoen A, Rasche F. Phenolics mediate suppression of *Fusarium oxysporum* f. sp. *cubense* TR4 by legume root exudates. Rhizosphere. 2022;**21**:100459

[152] Sadeghi M, Zolfaghari B, Senatore M, Lanzotti V. Spirostane, furostane and cholestane saponins from Persian leek with antifungal activity. Food Chemistry. 2013;**141**(2):1512–1521

[153] Khaliq G, Abbas HT, Ali I, Waseem M. Aloe vera gel enriched with garlic essential oil effectively controls anthracnose disease and maintains postharvest quality of banana fruit during storage. Horticulture, Environment, and Biotechnology. 2019;**60**(5):659–669

[154] Bhagat S, Dutta U, Mahajan T. Antifungal activity of important botanicals against plant pathogens. International Journal of Current Microbiology and Applied Sciences. 2019;**8**(10):531–545

[155] Smith A. A thorough assessment of biotechnological options for improving heavy metal tolerance in neglected and underused legume crops. Journal of Microbiology Reports. 2022;**5**(1):1–2

[156] Raqueti GS, Ferreira TC, Olivio MLG, Morais FAA, Coscione AR, Camargos LS. Emergence and N metabolism of *Canavalia ensiformis* (L.) DC. seedlings in soil contaminated by nickel. Notulae Botanicae Horti Agrobotanici Cluj-Napoca. 2025;**53**(1):1–12

[157] de Leon D P, Garcia Rubido M, Rivera R, Mancero-Castillo D, Garcia Y. Benefits of *Canavalia ensiformis*, arbuscular mycorrhizal fungi, and mineral fertilizer management in tobacco production. Frontiers in Agronomy. 2024;**6**:1422174

[158] Mohamad R, Maynaud G, Le Quéré A, Vidal C, Klonowska A, Yashiro E, et al. Ancient heavy metal contamination in soils as a driver of

tolerant *Anthyllis vulneraria* rhizobial communities. Applied and Environmental Microbiology. 2017;**83**(2):e02170–16

[159] Ojuederie OB, Popoola JO, Aremu C, Babalola OO. Harnessing the hidden treasures in African yam bean (*Sphenostylis stenocarpa*), an underutilized grain legume with food security potentials. In Food Security and Safety: African Perspectives Cham: Springer; 2021. p. 1–20

[160] Ojuederie OB, Ajiboye JA, Babalola OO. Biochemical and Histopathological Studies of Key Tissues in Healthy Male Wistar Rats Fed on African Yam Bean Seed and Tuber Meals. Journal of Food Quality. 2020;**2020**:1–10

[161] Osuagwu AN, Edem UL, Kalu SE. Evaluation of genetic diversity in aerial yam (*Dioscorea bulbifera* L) using qualitative and quantitative morphological traits. Global Scientific Journal. 2019;7(11):368–390

[162] Unachukwu NN, Menkir A, Rabbi IY, Oluoch M, Muranaka S, Elzein A, et al. Genetic diversity and population structure of Striga hermonthica populations from Kenya and Nigeria. Weed Research. 2017;**57**:293–302

[163] Aina AI, Ilori CO, Ekanem UO, Oyatomi O, Potter D, Abberton MT. Morphological characterization and variability analysis of African yam bean (*Sphenostylis stenocarpa* Hochst. ex. A. Rich) Harms. International Journal of Plant Research. 2020;**10**(3):45–52

[164] Agre P, Asibe F, Darkwa K, Edemodu A, Bauchet G, Asiedu R, et al. Phenotypic and molecular assessment of genetic structure and diversity in a panel of winged yam (*Dioscorea alata*) clones and cultivars. Scientific Reports 2019;**9**:18221

[165] Yang W, Kang X, Yang Q, Lin Y, Fang M. Review on the development of genotyping methods for assessing farm animal diversity. Journal of Animal Science and Biotechnology. 2013;**4**(1):2

[166] Lörz H, Wenzel G. Molecular marker systems in plant breeding and crop improvement. 2007

[167] Govindaraj M, Vetriventhan M, Srinivasan M. Importance of genetic diversity assessment in crop plants and its recent advances: An overview of its analytical perspectives. Genetics Research International. 2015;**2015**(1):431487

[168] Mabhaudhi T, Modi AT, Beletse YG. Growth, phenological and yield responses of a bambara groundnut (*Vigna subterranea* L. Verdc) landrace to imposed water stress: II. Rain shelter conditions. Water Sa. 2013;**39**(2):191–198

[169] Olanrewaju OS, Oyatomi O, Babalola OO, Abberton M. Genetic Diversity and Environmental Influence on Growth and Yield Parameters of Bambara Groundnut. Frontiers in Plant Science. 2021;**12**:784410

[170] Mogale TE. Multi-Location Field Evaluation of Bambara Groundnut (Vigna subterranean (L) Verdc) for Agronomic Performance and Seed Protein. 2018

[171] Gedil M, Ferguson M, Girma G, Gisel A Perspectives on the application of next-generation sequencing to the improvement of Africa's staple food

crops. In: Next generation sequencing: advances, applications and challenges. 2016;287–308. Cham: Springer

[172] Hickey JM, Chiurugwi T, Mackay I, Powell W. Genomic prediction unifies animal and plant breeding programs to form platforms for biological discovery. Nature Genetics. 2017;**49**(9):1297–1303

[173] Yang W, Feng H, Zhang X, Zhang J, Doonan JH, Batchelor WD, et al. Crop phenomics and high-throughput phenotyping: Past decades, current challenges, and future perspectives. Molecular Plant. 2020;**13**:187–214

[174] Okii D, Tukamuhabwa P, Odong T, Namayanja A, Mukabaranga J, Paparu P, et al. Morphological diversity of tropical common bean germplasm. African Crop Science Journal. 2014;**22**:59–68

[175] Ayo-Vaughan MA, Ariyo OJ, Alake CO. Combining ability and genetic components for pod and seed traits in cowpea lines. Italian Journal of Agronomy. 2013;**8**(2):e10

[176] Talukdar D. Comparative morpho-physiological and biochemical responses of lentil and grass pea genotypes under water stress. Journal of Natural Science, Biology, and Medicine. 2013;**4**(2):396

[177] Ajayi AT, Adekola MO, Taiwo BH, Azuh VO. Character expression and differences in yield potential of ten genotypes of cowpea (*Vigna unguiculata* L. Walp). International Journal of Plant Research. 2014;**4**(3):63–71

[178] Keskin SO, Ali TM, Ahmed J, Shaikh M, Siddiq M, Uebersax MA. Physico-chemical and functional properties of legume protein, starch, and dietary fiber—A review. Legume Science. 2022;**4**(1):e117

[179] Piepho HP, Möhring J. Computing heritability and selection response from unbalanced plant breeding trials. Genetics. 2007;**177**(3):1881–1888

[180] Budhlakoti N, Kushwaha AK, Rai A, Chaturvedi KK, Kumar A, Pradhan AK, et al Genomic selection: A tool for accelerating the efficiency of molecular breeding for development of climate-resilient crops. Frontiers in Genetics. 2022;**13**:832153

[181] Dwivedi SL, Siddique KHM, Farooq M, Thornton PK, Ortiz R. Using Biotechnology-Led Approaches to Uplift Cereal and Food Legume Yields in Dryland Environments. Frontiers in Plant Science. 2018;**9**:1029

[182] Desta ZA, Ortiz R. Genomic selection: Genome-wide prediction in plant improvement. Trends in Plant Science. 2014;**19**(9):592–601

[183] Rychel-Bielska S, Nazzicari N, Plewiński P, Bielski W, Annicchiarico P, Książkiewicz M. Development of PCR-based markers and whole-genome selection model for anthracnose resistance in white lupin (*Lupinus albus* L.). Journal of Applied Genetics. 2020;**61**(4):531–545

[184] Hawkins C, Yu LX. Recent progress in alfalfa (*Medicago sativa* L.) genomics and genomic selection. Crop Journal. 2018;**6**(6):565–575

[185] Edet OU, Gorafi YSA, Nasuda S, Tsujimoto H. DArTseq-based analysis of genomic relationships among species of tribe Triticeae. Scientific Reports. 2018;**8**(1):16397

[186] Barilli E, Cobos MJ, Carrillo E, Kilian A, Carling J, Rubiales D. A high-density integrated DArTseq SNP-based genetic map of Pisum fulvum and identification of QTLs controlling rust resistance. Frontiers in Plant Science. 2018;**9**:167

[187] Yang SY, Saxena RK, Kulwal PL, Ash GJ, Dubey A, Harper JDI, et al. The first genetic map of pigeon pea based on diversity arrays technology (DArT) markers. Journal of Genetics. 2011;**90**:103–109

[188] Oluwole OO, Olomitutu OE, Paliwal R, Oyatomi O, Abberton MT, Obembe O Preliminary assessment of the association between DArT-SEQ SNP and some nutritional traits in African yam bean. 2017

[189] Valdisser PAMR, Pereira WJ, Almeida Filho JE, Müller BSF, Coelho GRC, de Menezes IPP, et al. In-depth genome characterization of a Brazilian common bean core collection using DArTseq high-density SNP genotyping. BMC Genomics. 2017;**18**:423

[190] Mayes S, Basu S, Murchie E, Roberts JA, Azam-Ali SN, Stadler F, et al. BAMLINK-A Cross disciplinary programme to enhance the role of bambara groundnut (*Vigna subterranea* L. Verdc.) for food security in Africa and India. In: International Symposium on Underutilized Plants for Food Security, Nutrition, Income and Sustainable Development 806. 2008. p. 137–150

[191] McCouch S. Diversifying selection in plant breeding. PLoS Biology. 2004;**2** (10):e347

[192] Collard BCY, Mackill DJ. Marker-assisted selection: An approach for precision plant breeding in the twenty-first century. Philosophical Transactions of the Royal Society B: Biological Sciences. 2008;**363** (1491):557–572

[193] Rao NK. Plant genetic resources: Advancing conservation and use through biotechnology. African Journal of Biotechnology. 2004;**3**(2):136–145

[194] Ogunkanmi LA, Ogundipe OT, Ng NQ, Fatokun CA. Genetic diversity in wild relatives of cowpea (*Vigna unguiculata*) as revealed by simple sequence repeats (SSR) markers. Journal of Food, Agriculture & Environment. 2008;**6**(3&4):263–8

[195] Singh SP, Nodari R, Gepts P. Genetic diversity in cultivated common bean: I Allozymes. Crop Science. 1991;**31** (1):19–23

[196] Molina C, Rotter B, Horres R, Udupa SM, Besser B, Bellarmino L, et al. SuperSAGE: The drought stress-responsive transcriptome of chickpea roots. BMC Genomics. 2008;**9**:553

[197] Carpentier SC, Panis B, Vertommen A, Swennen R, Sergeant K, Renaut J, et al. Proteome analysis of non-model plants: A challenging but powerful approach. Mass Spectrometry Reviews. 2008;**27**:354–377

[198] Chakraborty S, Chakraborty N, Datta A. Increased nutritive value of transgenic potato by expressing a nonallergenic seed albumin gene from *Amaranthus hypochondriacus*. Proceedings of the National Academy of Sciences. 2000;**97**(7):3724–3729

[199] Chakraborty N, Chakraborty S, Rathi D. Proteomics of an orphan legume, grasspea: Current status and future strategy. Plant Tissue Culture and Biotechnology. 2015;**25**(1):117–141

[200] Bohra A, Pareek S, Jha R, Saxena RK, Singh IP, Pandey G, et al. Modern genomic tools for pigeonpea improvement: status and prospects. In: The pigeonpea genome. Cham: Springer; 2017. p. 41–54

[201] Horn R, Gupta KJ, Colombo N. Mitochondrion role in molecular basis of cytoplasmic male sterility. Mitochondrion. 2014;**19**:198–205

[202] Saxena KB, Hingane AJ. Male sterility systems in major field crops and their potential role in crop improvement. In Plant Biology and Biotechnology: Volume I: Plant Diversity, Organization, Function and Improvement Cham. Springer; 2015. p. 639–656

[203] Bohra A, Jha UC, Adhimoolam P, Bisht D, Singh NP. Cytoplasmic male sterility (CMS) in hybrid breeding in field crops. Plant Cell Reports. 2016;**35**(5):967–993

[204] Singh NP, Praharaj CS, Verma P. Progress towards self-sufficiency in pulses in India. Pulses Value Chain Development for Achieving Food and Nutrition Security in South Asia: Current Status and Future Prospectes. SAARC Agriculture Centre. 2019; 134. https://oar.icrisat.org/11707/1/Pandey%20and%20et.%20al._Pulses%20Value%20Chain%20Development%20in%20South%20Asia.pdf#page=147

[205] Bekkering CS, Tian L. Thinking outside of the cereal box: Breeding underutilized (pseudo) cereals for improved human nutrition. Frontiers in Genetics. 2019;**10**:1289

[206] Popoola JO, Ojuederie OB, Aworunse OS, Adelekan A, Oyelakin AS, Oyesola OL, et al Nutritional, functional, and bioactive properties of African underutilized legumes. Frontiers in Plant Science. 2023;**14**:1105364

[207] Majola NG. Verdc for enhanced yield and nutritional quality in South Africa [PhD thesis]. *Breeding Bambara groundnut (Vigna subterranea (L.)*. Pietermaritzburg: University of KwaZulu-Natal; 2023

[208] Nomathemba G. Breeding Bambara Groundnut (Vigna subterranea (L.) Verdc) for Enhanced Yield and Nutritional Quality in South Africa. 2023

[209] Coulibaly M, Bodjrenou G, Akohoue F, Agoyi EE, Merinosy Francisco FM, Agossou COA, et al. Profiling Cultivars Development in Kersting's Groundnut [*Macrotyloma geocarpum* (Harms) Maréchal and Baudet] for Improved Yield, Higher Nutrient Content, and Adaptation to Current and Future Climates. Frontiers in Sustainable Food Systems. 2022;**5**:942335

[210] Shitta NS, Edemodu AC, Abtew WG, Tesfaye AA. A review on the cooking attributes of African yam bean (*Sphenostylis stenocarpa*) . In Legumes Research-Volume 2. London, UK: IntechOpen; 2021. p. 391–45

[211] Das G, Sharma A, Sarkar PK. Conventional and emerging processing techniques for the post-harvest reduction of antinutrients in edible legumes. Applied Food Research. 2022;**2**(1):100112

Chapter 7

Bean Rust Disease in the Genomics Era: Pathogen Diversity, Resistance Breeding and Field Impact

Michael Lucas Daud, Papias H. Binagwa,
Susan Nchimbi-Msolla, Deusdedith R. Mbanzibwa,
Beatrice Victor Mwaipopo, Salma O. Mohhamed and
Luseko Amos Chilagane

Abstract

Common bean (*Phaseolus vulgaris* L.), an essential commodity in food and nutritional security for millions of people, is known for its adaptability to a wide range of agroecological environments. However, *P. vulgaris* productivity is persistently threatened by both biotic and abiotic stresses. In particular, *P. vulgaris* rust (a fungal disease caused by *Uromyces appendiculatus*) causes significant yield losses (over 70% under high disease pressure) and acts as a major barrier to achieving consistent and sustainable yields. This chapter aims to: (i) provide a comprehensive exploration of *P. vulgaris* rust disease and articulate its ongoing importance as a significant constraint to *P. vulgaris* productivity; (ii) synthesize the current scientific understanding of the vast diversity within pathogen populations; (iii) highlight the pivotal role of genomics and transcriptomics in advancing the grasp of the dynamic interactions between host *P. vulgaris* plants and the rust pathogen; (iv) outline the major methods and practicalities of phenotyping, race identification, and effective deployment of resistant cultivars across a range of agroecological contexts; and (v) illustrate the impact of deploying well-characterized resistance sources and improved cultivars through representative case studies. Overall, this chapter bridges scientific advancements with their tangible outcomes in the field. It also offers researchers, plant breeders, and agricultural practitioners a holistic perspective on leveraging pathogen genomics and resistance breeding to address the enduring challenge of *P. vulgaris* rust in real-world farming systems.

Keywords: *Phaseolus vulgaris*, *Uromyces appendiculatus*, host resistance, pathogen diversity, host-pathogen interactions, genomics-assisted breeding, population genomics, bean rust disease

Figure 1.
*Representation of the rust-affected leaves of common bean (*Phaseolus vulgaris *L.). Photo: M. Daud.*

1. Introduction

The common bean (*Phaseolus vulgaris* L.) stands as an essential commodity in food and nutritional security for millions of people, particularly across low and middle-income nations in sub-Saharan Africa and Latin America. It is cherished not only for its adaptability to a wide range of agroecological environments but also for its nutritional profile, which offers essential proteins and micronutrients crucial for balanced diets, nitrogen fixation, and an income source [1–5]. Despite its socio-economic importance, *P. vulgaris* productivity is persistently threatened by both biotic and abiotic stresses. Among these, fungal diseases, particularly bean rust caused by *Uromyces appendiculatus*, represent a major barrier to achieving consistent and sustainable yields, with typical symptoms on infected leaves shown in **Figure 1.** Under conducive environmental conditions and in susceptible cultivars, *P. vulgaris* rust can cause yield losses exceeding 70% under high disease pressure, a level of impact that underscores the urgency for effective management strategies [2, 6, 7]. Due to the need for legume crops that can cope with changing climates, managing rust disease has become a key focus for *P. vulgaris* breeding and plant health efforts around the world.

2. Pathogen biology and epidemiology

2.1 Life cycle and infection biology of *Uromyces appendiculatus*

U. appendiculatus is an autoecious, macrocyclic rust that completes its full cycle on *P. vulgaris* without requiring an alternate host, in contrast to the major wheat (*Triticum aestivum* L.) rusts that typically depend on two unrelated hosts to complete sexual reproduction [8–10]. As with many Uromyces rusts, the life cycle expresses five spore stages: pycniospores (spermatia), aeciospores, urediniospores, teliospores, and basidiospores. Urediniospores drive rapid, repeating infections during the season, whereas teliospores function as durable survival structures on infected residues and later germinate to initiate basidiospore production and sexual processes [9]. Upon successful colonization, the pathogen produces uredinia, which rupture through the leaf epidermis, manifesting as conspicuous rust-colored pustules predominantly on the underside of leaves (**Figure 2**) [11]. These pustules are highly prolific, generating vast quantities of urediniospores that are easily dispersed by air

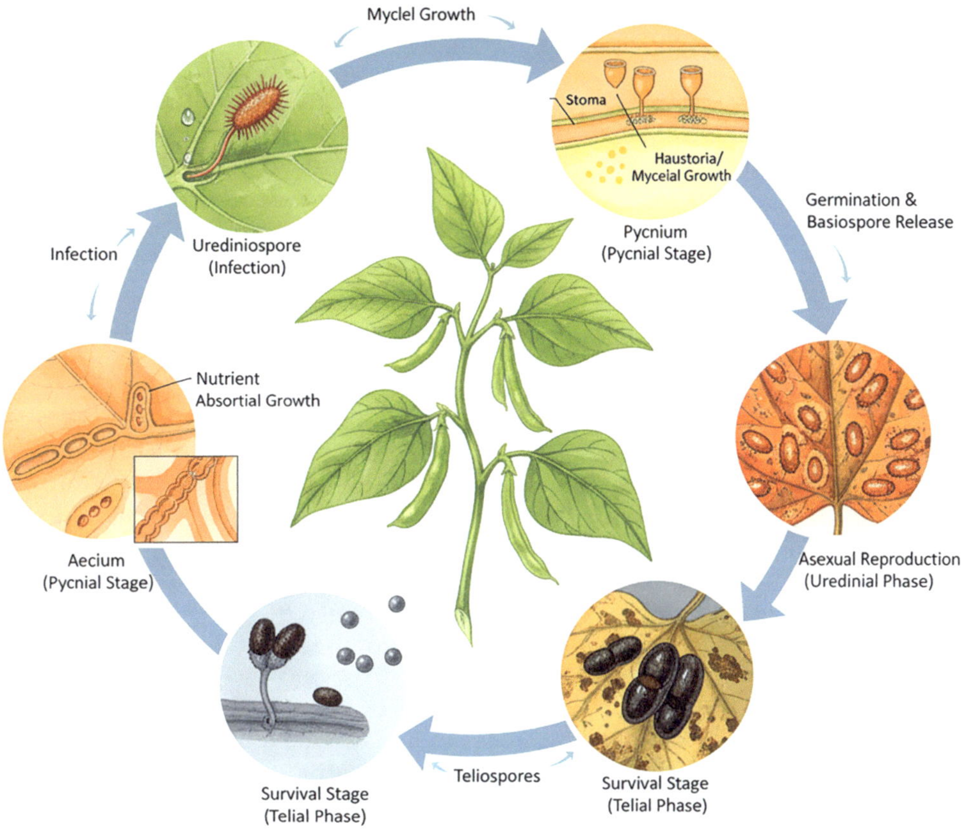

Figure 2.
*Representation of the disease cycle of common bean (*Phaseolus vulgaris *L.) rust. Modified after [11].*

currents, facilitating both local and regional spread of the disease. Under favorable environmental conditions, the uredinial cycle can repeat every 10 to 14 days, resulting in multiple rounds of infection and exponential increases in disease severity [12]. Among the life cycle stages (**Figure 2**), the uredinial phase stands out for its epidemiological significance. During this phase, the fungus reproduces asexually and rapidly, allowing for repeated cycles of reinfection within a single growing season [13]. The spores require the presence of free moisture to germinate, after which germ tubes penetrate the leaf through natural openings, primarily the stomata [13, 14]. Once inside, the fungus forms specialized structures called haustoria within the mesophyll cells for nutrient absorption and serves as delivery points for effector molecules that help the pathogen suppress the immune responses of *P. vulgaris* and maintain a persistent infection [15].

As the *P. vulgaris* crop matures or environmental conditions become less conducive, the fungus shifts toward producing teliospores (thick-walled spores) for overwintering. When conditions improve, teliospores germinate to form basidiospores, which may initiate new infections at the onset of the next growing season [12]. The ability of *U. appendiculatus* to reproduce rapidly via urediniospores while also persisting through teliospores underlines its resilience and the recurrent nature of *P. vulgaris* rust in many *P. vulgaris*-growing regions worldwide [16].

2.2 Environmental drivers, transmission, and inoculum dynamics

P. vulgaris rust epidemics develop when host susceptibility, inoculum availability, and a "wet–cool" canopy microclimate coincide. Field and controlled-environment studies consistently show that rust increases under moderate temperatures and high humidity, particularly when free moisture persists on leaves for long periods. For example, disease development has been reported to peak around 20–25 °C with relative humidity above ~85% and extended leaf wetness (often 18–24 h) [17]. Complementary evidence indicates that cooler conditions (about 16–24 °C) combined with humid weather and prolonged leaf wetness (about 10–24 h) are conducive, and that urediniospore germination can occur within ~ 6–8 h when moisture and temperature are favorable [7]. Within a season, urediniospores drive most secondary spread because they are produced in large numbers in uredinia that rupture and release spores repeatedly during the *P. vulgaris* crop cycle [7]. Once established, rust can expand outward from initial foci quickly under conducive weather; in Ethiopian field conditions, disease foci were observed to expand on the order of centimeters per day (approximately 3.1–15.6 cm/day), underscoring how rapidly local epidemics can build when moisture and temperature remain favorable [18].

Between seasons, inoculum carryover is strengthened by "green bridges" and infected plant material. Volunteer beans arising from seeds left after harvest can support the pathogen and even allow completion of sexual development, which has implications for both survival and the generation of new variation [16]. In practical terms, this means that volunteer management and residue handling are not merely hygiene steps; they can influence the amount and continuity of inoculum that initiates early infections in the next crop. Altitude and agroecological settings often act as "risk multipliers" because they package temperature and moisture regimes in predictable ways. Surveys in Kenya explicitly note that rust occurrence is influenced by altitude, agronomic practices, temperature, relative humidity, and leaf surface moisture, and they document rust across zones spanning roughly ~ 1027–2,429 m a.s.l., with crop spacing and residue management significantly associated with disease severity [19].

3. Diversity of *uromyces appendiculatus* populations

The global landscape of *U. appendiculatus* is marked by remarkable race diversity, posing significant challenges to the sustainable deployment of host resistance. Over 250 distinct physiological races have been cataloged worldwide, primarily using differential *P. vulgaris* cultivars. These races are generally grouped into two major virulence lineages: Andean and Middle American, reflecting the evolutionary divergence of the *P. vulgaris* gene pools [20, 21]. Race classification relies on a standardized panel of differential cultivars, each carrying specific *Ur* resistance genes. These cultivars, such as Early Gallatin (*Ur*-4), Golden Gate Wax (*Ur*-3), and PI181,996 (*Ur*-11), have been instrumental in surveys across North and Latin America [22] (**Table 1**). A particular race is defined by its pattern of virulence (ability to infect) or avirulence (inability to infect) on this panel. However, as new virulence combinations emerge, the reliability of this system hinges on ongoing surveillance and regular updates to the set of differentials [23, 24].

Differential cultivar/line	Gene pool	*Ur* resistance gene(s)
Early Gallatin	Andean	*Ur*-4
Redlands Pioneer	Andean	*Ur*-13
Montcalm	Andean	Unnamed/unknown
Pompadour Checa-50 (PC-50)	Andean	*Ur*-9, *Ur*-12
Golden Gate Wax	Andean	*Ur*-6
PI 260,418	Andean	Unnamed/unknown (sometimes denoted *Ur–P*)
Great Northern 1,140	Mesoamerican	*Ur*-7
Aurora	Mesoamerican	*Ur*-3
Mexico 309	Mesoamerican	*Ur*-5
Mexico 235	Mesoamerican	*Ur*-3 +
Compuesto Negro Chimaltenango (CNC)	Mesoamerican	Unnamed/unknown (often denoted *Ur-CNC*)
PI 181,996	Mesoamerican	*Ur*-11

Table 1.
*Representation of the major standard differentials of common bean (*Phaseolus vulgaris *L.) [19, 25].*

Research has revealed increasing complexity in virulence, with races now capable of overcoming multiple *Ur* genes, including those previously considered robust when stacked together. Such races have been identified in East Africa, the United States, and Latin America, often following periods of intense rust pressure or widespread planting of resistant cultivars [6, 20, 21]. This trend underlines the need for dynamic resistance strategies and continuous monitoring of pathogen populations.

The dynamic and diverse nature of *U. appendiculatus* populations has significant implications for breeding and deploying resistant *P. vulgaris* varieties. Resistance based on single *Ur* genes is inherently fragile in the face of evolving pathogen races. For example, the increasing prevalence of races of *P. vulgaris* rust fungus able to overcome *Ur-3* and *Ur-11* genes in areas where *P. vulgaris* genotypes with these genes are widely deployed underscores the risk of resistance breakdown [2]. This reality is driving a shift toward strategies such as gene pyramiding, quantitative resistance, and the use of marker-assisted selection (MAS) to develop cultivars with more durable resistance. The characterized candidate genes are detailed in **Table 2** below.

4. Host–pathogen interactions in the genomics era

Research on *P. vulgaris* rust has moved from symptom description and race cataloging to genome-enabled studies that explain mechanisms underlying resistance and virulence. Nonetheless, race identification using differential cultivars remains fundamental for surveillance and breeding decisions [29, 30]. Genomic tools now link phenotypes to pathogen effectors and to host defense networks activated during infection [15, 24, 31]. Increasingly, multi-omics datasets are combined with genetic mapping to identify loci for both qualitative and quantitative resistance, and these discoveries are translated into marker-assisted selection and

Ur gene	Canonical source genotype (gene differential)	Gene pool
Ur-1	B1,627 (Gallaroy genotype I)	Mesoamerican
Ur-2	B2090 (Gallaroy genotype II)	Mesoamerican
Ur-3	Aurora	Mesoamerican
Ur-3 +	Mexico 235; Mexico & Ecuador 235/299 (reported); Ecuador 299;; 51,052/ 51,051	Mesoamerican
Ur-4	Early Gallatin; Brown Beauty	Andean
Ur-5	Mexico 309	Mesoamerican
Ur-6	Golden Gate Wax	Andean
Ur-6 +	Olathe (Pinto Olathe)	Andean/ Mesoamerican
Ur-7	Great Northern 1140	Mesoamerican
Ur-8	U.S. #3	Andean
Ur-9	PC-50	Andean
Ur-10	Resisto	Andean
Ur-11	PI 181,996	Mesoamerican
Ur-12	PC-50; PI 260,418 sometimes associated with an unnamed Andean gene (*Ur*–P)	Andean
Ur-13	Redlands Pioneer	Andean
Ur-14	Ouro Negro	Mesoamerican
Ur-22	AxS 37	Mesoamerican

Table 2.
*Representation of the major characterized candidate genes for common bean (*Phaseolus vulgaris *L.) Rust resistance and their sources [25–28].*

resistance gene pyramiding to improve durability [26, 32]. This approach aligns with integrated breeding and management recommendations for durable control [33].

Rust fungi deploy secreted effector proteins to suppress host immunity and promote colonization. In *U. appendiculatus*, candidate effectors have been prioritized based on strong haustorial expression and secretion signals, and several suppress PTI and ETI in functional assays, highlighting their role in immune evasion [30].

Multi-omics studies show that rust infection triggers broad host reprogramming, including large sets of differentially expressed genes associated with transcriptional regulation, detoxification (e.g., cytochrome P450s), stress protection, and pathogenesis-related functions [34]. Metabolomic shifts in flavonoids, phenylpropanoids, lipids, and related compounds indicate activation of secondary metabolism and stress responses [2, 34]. Evidence from integrated ChIP-seq/RNA-seq further suggests that histone modification dynamics shape defense-related gene expression during infection [35].

The gene-for-gene model remains a key framework for rust resistance (Flor, 1955, as cited in [36]), and *Ur* genes continue to underpin race differentiation and cultivar development [4, 37]. However, transcriptomic and metabolomic evidence supports additive, network-based defense responses consistent with quantitative resistance, which is often more durable due to reduced selection for virulent races

[8, 37, 38]. Integrating effector repertoires with R-gene mapping can also strengthen the prediction of resistance breakdown and inform diagnostic marker development [31].

Phenotyping and race characterization remain essential, but genomic tools add predictive and operational value. Key applications include (i) effector-informed germplasm screening [14, 31, 33], (ii) marker-assisted selection and gene pyramiding for durable resistance [24, 32, 39], (iii) pathogen population monitoring to track shifting virulence patterns across regions [19, 23, 27, 40], and (iv) multi-omics integration to connect mechanisms to breeding decisions [15, 33, 35, 41]. Where fungicide reliance is limited, combining surveillance with marker-assisted breeding remains a practical pathway for stable rust control [19, 33].

5. Resistance breeding strategies for bean rust

The high genetic and virulence variability of *Uromyces appendiculatus*, coupled with its capacity for rapid adaptation and persistence, necessitates forward-thinking resistance breeding strategies. Although traditional reliance on single major resistance genes and phenotypic screening has yielded short-term successes, these strategies often falter when confronted with emerging virulent races [42]. Modern breeding efforts are thus shifting toward combining multiple resistance mechanisms, exploiting both major and quantitative loci, and leveraging molecular and genomic innovations to develop cultivars with broad and durable resistance.

5.1 Major gene (qualitative) resistance: Strengths and constraints

Major gene, or qualitative, resistance is typically conferred by one or a few Mendelian R genes that provide high levels of protection against specific pathogen races. In *P. vulgaris*, several *Ur* genes have been characterized and widely used in breeding and variety release [4, 37]. These genes are relatively easy to track, especially with the aid of molecular markers, and confer strong resistance under initial deployment. However, qualitative resistance is inherently race-specific. As pathogen populations evolve new virulence alleles, formerly effective resistance can collapse, often resulting in severe epidemics. Empirical evidence shows that *Ur* genes have been overcome in multiple regions following the emergence of novel races [37, 43]. Furthermore, the deployment of single major genes can accelerate pathogen adaptation by exerting strong selection pressure. Consequently, while qualitative resistance remains a valuable tool, it cannot serve as the sole foundation for sustainable rust management.

5.2 Quantitative and partial resistance: Toward durable protection

In light of the vulnerabilities of single-gene resistance, breeders are increasingly prioritizing quantitative resistance. This form of resistance is governed by multiple genes or quantitative trait loci (QTL), each contributing incrementally to disease suppression. Quantitative resistance is typically expressed as reduced pustule density, slower disease progression, lower spore production, and extended latent periods [4, 19]. Although it seldom confers complete immunity, it is often sufficient to maintain economically viable yields under moderate to high disease pressure, especially when integrated with sound agronomic practices. A key advantage of quantitative resistance is its broad-spectrum nature; it does not depend on the recognition of specific pathogen avirulence genes, generally provides protection against a wider range of races, and is less likely to be rapidly overcome. This resilience makes quantitative resistance a crucial component in breeding pipelines targeting long-term, sustainable control of *P. vulgaris* rust [33, 38, 44].

5.3 Gene pyramiding: Combining multiple resistance sources

Gene pyramiding, the process of combining multiple resistance genes: both qualitative and quantitative into a single genotype, is a powerful strategy to enhance resistance durability and spectrum [45]. Recent breeding programs have demonstrated the feasibility of pyramiding major *Ur* genes with quantitative loci using molecular markers for precise tracking. For example, in Sri Lanka, breeders successfully combined *Ur-3* and *Ur-11* genes in snap-bean lines, generating over 400 genotypes with stable rust resistance over successive generations [46]. These lines retained favorable agronomic traits, underscoring the practical benefits of pyramiding for cultivar development. The success of gene pyramiding is greatly facilitated by marker-assisted selection (MAS), which allows for the simultaneous selection of multiple resistance alleles and accelerates breeding cycles. When pyramided with quantitative resistance loci, the resulting cultivars can achieve both high initial resistance and long-term durability, providing robust protection against evolving pathogen populations [32, 44, 47].

5.4 Genomics assisted breeding: MAS, genomic selection, and integrated approaches

The integration of genomics, sequencing technologies, and bioinformatics has revolutionized resistance breeding. In *P. vulgaris*, the availability of reference genomes, dense SNP arrays, and genotyping-by-sequencing (GBS) platforms supports both MAS and genomic selection (GS) [48–50]. MAS enables breeders to select for resistance alleles at early generations, independent of disease pressure in the environment, and is especially valuable for tracking multiple genes in pyramiding schemes. Genomic selection, which leverages genome-wide marker data to predict phenotypes such as resistance, yield, and adaptation, offers a means to capture both major and minor effect loci, epistatic interactions, and complex traits associated with disease resilience [51]. By integrating phenotypic and genomic data through approaches such as genome-wide association studies (GWAS), breeders can identify novel resistance loci, validate their efficacy across diverse germplasm, and refine breeding strategies to suit specific agroecological zones. This integrative, data-driven approach is increasingly recognized as the most promising avenue for sustainable rust management [33, 52].

6. Genomics-assisted breeding and molecular tools

6.1 Marker assisted selection (MAS) and its application in common bean

Marker-assisted selection (MAS) in *P. vulgaris* rust breeding is most useful when breeders can track specific rust-resistance genes during backcrossing and pyramiding using tightly linked PCR-based markers. In Brazil, a carioca-bean pyramiding program combined *Ur-5*, *Ur-11*, and *Ur-14* and screened segregating generations with markers SI19 (*Ur-5*), SAE19 (*Ur-11*), and OPX11 (*Ur-14*) to select lines carrying all target alleles before yield testing [32]. In Sri Lanka, *Ur-11* was introgressed from PI 181996 into local snap bean backgrounds and tracked using GT-2 (SCAR) and SAE19 (SCAR), together with OPAC20 (RAPD), during early-generation selection [53]. Follow-up pyramiding for broader resistance introgressed *Ur-3* and *Ur-11*, using SK14 (SCAR; *Ur-3*) alongside an SI-19 marker used for *Ur-11* tracking in that breeding pipeline [46]. A classic example of marker utility for rust gene stacking is the RAPD marker OA14_1,100, reported as tightly linked to Up-2, enabling more efficient pyramiding, especially when the marker is absent in the recurrent background [54].

6.2 Genome-wide association studies (GWAS) and trait mapping in bean

The application of genome-wide association studies (GWAS) has revolutionized the ability to dissect the genetic underpinnings of complex traits in *P. vulgaris*. GWAS leverages the natural genetic diversity present in broad germplasm collections to uncover associations between molecular markers and phenotypic traits, spanning both major and subtle genetic contributors [47, 49, 55]. Although GWAS focused specifically on *P. vulgaris* rust resistance remains relatively limited, analogous studies targeting other fungal diseases have demonstrated the method's powerful utility. These investigations have identified quantitative trait loci (QTLs) that confer resistance under field conditions, suggesting that GWAS holds substantial potential for advancing rust resistance breeding as well [49]. The diagnostic markers developed through GWAS can subsequently be implemented in MAS [56] or genomic selection pipelines, equipping breeders with flexible tools to track and combine favorable alleles across diverse genetic backgrounds and breeding cycles.

6.3 Genomic selection (GS) and prediction of complex traits

While MAS and GWAS are particularly effective for traits controlled by major genes or discrete QTL, many agronomic characteristics, including disease resistance expressed under variable field conditions, are polygenic and influenced by myriad loci, each contributing small effects. Genomic selection (GS) addresses this complexity by utilizing comprehensive genome-wide marker data to estimate breeding values for individual plants, thus enabling selection based on predicted, rather than solely observed, performance [39, 48, 57]. The application of GS has gained momentum in *P. vulgaris* breeding, with studies demonstrating its capacity to accurately predict yield components and biomass traits within interspecific hybrid populations, even under environmental stresses [48]. By facilitating simultaneous selection for multiple traits, such as resistance, yield, and adaptation, GS accelerates breeding cycles and enhances genetic gain per generation. This is particularly transformative for smallholder systems, where environmental heterogeneity is high and resources are limited, making resilience and multi-trait adaptability critical breeding objectives.

6.4 Emerging genomic and bioinformatics tools

Beyond the foundational genomics-assisted approaches, an array of emerging tools and resources is expanding the possibilities for *P. vulgaris* breeding. Pan-genome analyses, enabled by the increasing availability of germplasm panels and landrace collections, allow breeders to identify novel resistance alleles and structural variations, such as presence/absence or copy number changes, that may not exist in elite cultivars but are prevalent in traditional or wild accessions. This diversity is crucial for broadening the genetic base of resistance and mitigating the risks associated with genetic uniformity. Genomic visualization platforms, including introgression browsers like IBROWSER, provide detailed insights into the transfer and maintenance of resistance loci from wild relatives or landraces within elite lines. These tools facilitate the precise monitoring of introgression events at the SNP level, ensuring that essential resistance genes are retained while minimizing linkage drag [31, 58]. Another frontier, enviromics-informed prediction models, integrates genomic information with environmental variables such as climate, soil characteristics, and management practices. This approach has been applied successfully in smart breeding programs by integrating environmental descriptors with genomic prediction to better capture G × E and improve selection decisions across diverse target environments [59–61]. Such approaches are particularly pertinent for smallholder systems, where environmental variability necessitates regionally adapted solutions.

7. Field-level impacts

7.1 Prevalence, severity, and yield losses under smallholder conditions

Field-based studies across major *P. vulgaris*-producing regions have unequivocally demonstrated that *P. vulgaris* rust, driven by *U. appendiculatus*, remains a significant constraint for smallholder farmers. In comprehensive surveys conducted across five counties in western and central Kenya, researchers evaluated 77 local *P. vulgaris* genotypes under natural infection conditions, meticulously recording rust incidence and severity, and conducting greenhouse inoculation tests for the most aggressive local races [19]. The findings revealed widespread rust distribution and high disease severity, with a substantial proportion of smallholder-grown genotypes exhibiting susceptibility.

Parallel studies in Uganda have reinforced these observations, highlighting the substantial yield losses incurred by farmers during rust epidemics. Experimental data indicate that susceptible cultivars can experience yield reductions surpassing 70 percent under natural infection, while resistant genotypes suffer markedly less loss [4]. Historical research from Ethiopia further accentuates the devastating potential of rust, documenting cases of near-total crop failure and yield reductions ranging from 10 to 100 percent during severe epidemics [18]. These field-level realities are especially pertinent in smallholder contexts, where limited access to fungicides and other high-input solutions amplifies the impact of rust outbreaks. The data underscore three critical points: rust pressure is persistent and geographically widespread; yield losses under real-world, low-input management are often severe; and the adoption of resistant cultivars provides a tangible means to buffer yield declines and stabilize production.

Year	Area harvested (Mha)	Yield (t/ha)	Production (Mt)
2014	31.003	0.82	25.409
2015	31.607	0.83	26.292
2016	35.533	0.77	27.231
2017	37.382	0.78	29.287
2018	36.335	0.76	27.504
2019	33.427	0.76	25.507
2020	34.916	0.78	27.397
2021	37.412	0.76	28.337
2022	37.768	0.75	28.338
2023	37.751	0.76	28.506

Source: FAOSTAT, Production: Crops and Livestock Products (accessed 26 Dec 2025).

Table 3.
*Representation of the global production trend of common beans (*Phaseolus vulgaris *L.) (2014–2023).*

7.2 Socioeconomic and systemic implications for smallholder farming systems

P. vulgaris underpins both diets and cash flow in many smallholder systems. Globally, it is grown on about 30 million hectares (**Table 3**), and in Africa on ~7.6 million hectares, where it is consumed and traded by more than 100 million households [57]. Demand is also reflected in consumption intensity; per-capita consumption of 40–60 kg year^{-1} has been reported for Rwanda, Kenya, and Uganda [57]. However, earlier household data from Kenya showed strong consumption even among low-income groups [62]. At the same time, productivity remains modest across many *P. vulgaris*-growing areas [57]. *P. vulgaris* rust amplifies this vulnerability because it reduces both harvestable grain and marketable surplus. Under conducive conditions, susceptible cultivars can suffer very high yield losses [19], and field experiments in Uganda recorded substantial yield reductions in susceptible materials compared with more resistant entries [4]. Recent field surveillance also demonstrates how widespread the threat can be; in southern Ethiopia, 90% of surveyed fields were affected, with mean incidence and severity varying markedly by location and management [6]. Where fungicides are used, control can be effective, but repeated sprays raise cash costs that many smallholders struggle to absorb, especially in systems dominated by recycled seed and limited access to quality inputs [19].

8. Conclusions and recommendations

8.1 Conclusion

This chapter provides a comprehensive review of the current understanding regarding *Uromyces appendiculatus*, a *P. vulgaris* rust disease causal pathogen. It covers the pathogen's biology, the diversity found within its populations, and advances in genomics, alongside an evaluation of breeding strategies for resistance and their impact on smallholder *P. vulgaris* farmers. The collected evidence demonstrates the pathogen's capacity for adaptation and its varied virulence, which underscores the importance of robust surveillance and molecular diagnostic techniques. Effective management of *P. vulgaris* rust calls for sustainable strategies that extend beyond reliance on single resistance genes. Approaches such as quantitative resistance, stacking multiple resistance genes, and breeding programs informed by genomic data are essential. Combining advanced genomic technologies with ongoing monitoring, precise agronomic practices, and strategic deployment of resistance traits presents the most promising route forward, particularly for smallholder farming systems. Results from field trials consistently show that integrating resistant *P. vulgaris* varieties within broader disease management frameworks leads to significant reductions in yield losses. Success is maximized when resistance is tailored to the specific pathogen populations and environmental conditions present locally.

Looking ahead, the management of *P. vulgaris* rust will benefit from the convergence of genomics, molecular biology, and epidemiological research. Ensuring sustainable *P. vulgaris* production will require not only technological innovation but also coordinated efforts, strong institutional backing, and strategies that are sensitive to local contexts. Collaboration among scientists, plant breeders, extension professionals, policy makers, and farmers will be crucial in developing *P. vulgaris* varieties resilient to rust and other threats. This chapter aimed to guide future research and action, highlighting the need for scientific progress to translate into practical benefits for smallholder farmers and to contribute to global food security.

8.2 Key knowledge gaps and limitations

Despite significant progress, several critical gaps and barriers limit the effectiveness of current *Phaseolus vulgaris* rust management efforts:

i. Incomplete nucleotide sequences of rust pathogen: Genome assemblies for the rust pathogen *Uromyces appendiculatus* remain incomplete, which constrains the full exploitation of comparative genomics for resistance gene discovery, pathogen characterization, and the development of targeted diagnostic tools.

ii. Limited molecular epidemiology information: There is scant molecular epidemiological information on pathogen populations in many *P. vulgaris*-producing regions, particularly in Sub-Saharan Africa. This gap hinders comprehensive mapping of race diversity, delays the identification of emerging virulent strains, and reduces the effectiveness of the planting material deployed for rust resistance.

iii. Validation of quantitative resistance: Many resistance loci identified through research require further validation in a range of environments, especially in smallholder systems that experience diverse biotic and abiotic stresses. Without thorough field validation, the durability and practical value of quantitative resistance remain uncertain.

iv. Institutional and capacity constraints: A lack of trained personnel, insufficient infrastructure, and limited financial resources may delay the adoption and scaling of advanced breeding technologies and seed system improvements, particularly in resource-constrained settings.

v. Socio-economic and adoption barriers: Socio-economic factors, including farmer preferences, seed accessibility, end-use quality, and market demands, are not yet fully understood or addressed in many breeding and dissemination programs. More targeted socio-economic research and engagement are needed to ensure that technological advancements lead to real-world impact and widespread uptake.

Strategically addressing the highlighted knowledge gaps and limitations through targeted research, robust capacity building, and inclusive, multi-stakeholder collaboration will be essential for developing resilient *P. vulgaris* varieties and sustainable management frameworks that safeguard food security and farmer livelihoods amid evolving challenges.

8.3 Recommendations for bean rust management

Addressing common *P. vulgaris* rust disease effectively requires a suite of interconnected strategies that blend cutting-edge research with practical field solutions tailored for smallholder farmers. The expanded recommendations below aim to promote sustainable *P. vulgaris* production, enhance resilience against multiple challenges, and ensure research progress translates into on-the-ground impact:

i. Broaden genetic diversity: Expand the screening of *P. vulgaris* germplasm to include a wider array of landraces, wild relatives, and underutilized genetic resources from diverse geographic origins. Employ advanced genomics and phenotyping technologies to identify and incorporate novel resistance genes, thereby fortifying the breeding pool against evolving pathogen pressures and broadening the spectrum of resistance available to breeders.

ii. Enhance pathogen surveillance and monitoring: Establish regional and national networks that systematically collect and analyze *Uromyces appendiculatus* samples using both traditional race typing and molecular diagnostics interactively. Regular monitoring should document shifts in pathogen virulence and genetic diversity, enabling rapid updates of breeding priorities and guiding localized management strategies.

iii. Implement genomics-guided breeding: Create robust breeding pipelines that integrate marker-assisted selection, genomic prediction, and high-throughput phenotyping. Focus on balancing rust resistance with desirable agronomic traits such as yield, market class, and adaptation to local environments. Multi-location field trials should rigorously evaluate new lines across varied agro-ecological settings to ensure stable and widely effective resistance.

iv. Strengthen seed systems: Support the development of quality seed production infrastructure, as well as participatory, community-managed seed supplies that empower local farmers. Ensure varietal integrity through quality assurance measures, and foster mechanisms for rapid, equitable distribution of improved seed. Involve farmers directly in the evaluation, selection, and multiplication processes to build trust and increase adoption rates.

v. Adopt an integrated disease management strategy to control *P. vulgaris* rust: Combine genetic strategies with complementary agronomic practices such as crop rotation, optimal planting schedules, residue management, and timely application of biocontrol agents or fungicides. Develop accessible training modules and decision-support tools tailored to the needs and constraints of smallholder farmers, enabling them to implement integrated management approaches effectively.

vi. Pursue multi-stress resistance: Target the development of *P. vulgaris* varieties that combine robust rust resistance with tolerance or resilience to abiotic stresses such as drought, heat, and poor soils. Use climate-resilience screening protocols and interdisciplinary collaboration to breed cultivars capable of thriving under future climate scenarios, thus "future-proofing" *P. vulgaris* production systems.

vii. Institutional support and collaboration: Invest in the capacity of research institutions and extension agencies by providing funding, training, and opportunities for collaboration among scientists, breeders, policy makers, and farmers. Promote interdisciplinary and cross-sectoral partnerships to accelerate the transfer of knowledge from research to practice and ensure sustained progress in disease management.

viii. Adopt dynamic resistance management approaches: Proactively rotate or stack diverse resistance genes within and among cultivars across growing seasons and geographic regions to outpace pathogen adaptation. Integrate surveillance data to inform resistance deployment, and encourage the use of integrated agronomic practices that collectively lower disease pressure and prolong resistance durability.

ix. Integrate disease forecasting: Develop and operationalize predictive models that synthesize climate, weather, and pathogen monitoring data to provide timely, context-specific recommendations for disease prevention and control. Extension services should ensure that farmers receive actionable advice tailored to their unique agro-ecological and socio-economic circumstances.

x. Strengthen the active engagement of smallholder farmers throughout the research-to-use continuum, including the co-development, on-farm evaluation, dissemination, and effective utilization of improved varieties and complementary management innovations. Institutionalize participatory plant breeding approaches and structured knowledge-sharing platforms that value farmers' expertise, preferences, and production constraints. This will enhance the relevance and acceptability of innovations, improve long-term sustainability, and reinforce the uptake of quality-assured seed through formal seed systems.

Acknowledgments

The authors sincerely thank the Tanzania Commission for Science and Technology (COSTECH) through the National Fund for Advancement of Science and Technology (NFAST) program [Reg. No. FA.403/489/206] for financial support. These contributions are acknowledged as non-author contributions in line with standard authorship criteria, and all authors take responsibility for the final content of the chapter.

The author acknowledges the use of Microsoft Copilot (embedded in Microsoft 365) for language polishing and Google Gemini AI for the creation of **Figure 2** in the manuscript.

Conflict of Interest

The authors declare no conflict of interest.

Author details

Michael Lucas Daud[1,2]*, Papias H. Binagwa[3], Susan Nchimbi-Msolla[2], Deusdedith R. Mbanzibwa[4], Beatrice Victor Mwaipopo[2], Salma O. Mohhamed[5] and Luseko Amos Chilagane[2]

1 Sokoine University of Agriculture (SUA), Department of Agricultural Sciences, Katavi, Tanzania

2 Department of Crop Science and Horticulture, Sokoine University of Agriculture (SUA), Morogoro, Chuo Kikuu, Morogoro, Tanzania

3 Tanzania Agricultural Research Institute (TARI), Selian Centre, Arusha, Tanzania

4 Tanzania Agricultural Research Institute (TARI), Dodoma, Tanzania

5 Zanzibar Agricultural and Livestock Research Institute (ZALIRI), Dole- Mjini Magharibi, Tanzania

*Address all correspondence to: michael.daud@sua.ac.tz

References

[1] Broughton WJ, Hernández G, Blair M, Beebe S, Gepts P, Vanderleyden J Beans (Phaseolus spp.) - Model food legumes. In: Plant and Soil. 2003. p. 55–128. Available from: https://www.researchgate.net/publication/226474316_Beans_Phaseolus_spp_-_Model_food_legumes [Accessed: 2025-December-07]

[2] Makhumbila P, Rauwane ME, Muedi HH, Madala NE, Figlan S. Metabolome profile variations in common bean (Phaseolus vulgaris L.) resistant and susceptible genotypes incited by rust (Uromyces appendiculatus). Frontiers in Genetics. 2023;**14**(3):1–13. DOI: 10.3389/fgene.2023.1141201/full

[3] Martins D, de S AS, Rubiales D, Patto MCV. Legume crops and biotrophic pathogen interactions: A continuous cross-talk of a multilayered array of defense mechanisms. Plants. 2020;**9**(11):1–24

[4] Odogwu BA, Nkalubo ST, Rubaihayo P. Yield loss of common bean caused by rust disease in Uganda. J Underutilized Legum Soc Underutilized Legum. 2021;**3**(1):1–12

[5] Beebe SE, Rao IM, Blair MW, Acosta-Gallegos JA. Phenotyping common beans for adaptation to drought. Frontiers in Physiology. 2013;**4**(35):1–20. DOI: 10.3389/fphys.2013.00035/full

[6] Tsegaye Y, Chala A, Rezene Y. Destructive fungal disease survey of common bean (Phaseolus vulgaris L.) rust (Uromyces appendiculatus) in Southern Ethiopia. Scientific Reports. 2024;**14**(1):23642. DOI: 10.1038/s41598-024-72576-9

[7] Bhandari S, Thapa A, Bhandari S, Karkidholi P, Saud B, S KC, et al. Integrated approach for the management of common bean rust (Uromyces appendiculatus) under field conditions. Archives of Agriculture and Environmental Science 2023;**8**:377–384

[8] Makhumbila P, Rauwane M, Muedi H, Madala NE, Figlan S. Exploring associations between metabolites and gene transcripts of common bean (Phaseolus vulgaris L.) in response to rust (Uromyces appendiculatus) infection. BMC Plant Biology. 2025;**25**(1). DOI: 10.1186/s12870-025-06584-w

[9] Gautam AK, Avasthi S, Verma RK, Sushma, Niranjan M, Devadatha B, et al. A Global Overview of Diversity and Phylogeny of the Rust Genus Uromyces. Journal of Fungi. 2022;**8**. Available from: https://www.mdpi.com/2309-608X/8/6/633 [Accessed: 2025-December-08]

[10] Kleczewski N, Bradley C, Chilvers M, Collins A, DeWolf E, Friskop A, et al. An Overview of Stripe Rust of Wheat. United States; 2020. Available from: https://cropprotectionnetwork.org/publications/an-overview-of-stripe-rust-of-wheat [Accessed: 2025-December-06]

[11] Field Crop Diseases Victoria. Rust of faba bean. Field Crop Diseases. 2020. p. 1. Available from: https://extensionaus.com.au/FieldCropDiseasesVic/docs/identification-management-of-field-crop-diseases-in-victoria/faba-

beans/rust-of-faba-bean/ [Accessed: 2025-September-10]

[12] Rajendran L, Chellappan G. Uromyces. In: Natarajan A, Krishina K, editors. Compendium of Phytopathogenic Microbes in Agro-Ecology. Cham: Springer Nature Switzerland; 2025. p. 873–908. DOI: 10.1007/978-3-031-81 770-0_37

[13] Chung WH, Tsukiboshi T, Ono Y, Kakishima M. Morphological and phylogenetic analyses of Uromyces appendiculatus and U. vignae on legumes in Japan. Mycoscience. 2004;**45** (4):233–244. DOI: 10.1007/S10267-004-0177-9

[14] Link TI, Lang P, Scheffler BE, V. DM, Graham MA, Cooper B, et al. The haustorial transcriptomes of Uromyces appendiculatus and Phakopsora pachyrhizi and their candidate effector families. Molecular Plant Pathology. 2014;**15**(4):379–393. DOI: 10.1111/mpp.12099

[15] Link TI. Testing reference genes for transcript profiling in Uromyces appendiculatus during urediospore infection of common bean. PLoS One. 2020;**15**(8):1–15. DOI: 10.1371/journal.pone.0237273

[16] McMillan MS, Schwartz HF, Otto KL. Sexual stage development of Uromyces appendiculatus and its potential use for disease resistance screening of Phaseolus vulgaris. Plant Disease. 2003;**87**(9):1133–1138. DOI: 10.1094/PDIS.2003.87.9.1133

[17] Singh G, Gupta SK. Role of temperature, relative humidity and rainfall in the development of French bean rust (Uromyces appendiculatus). Indian Phytopathology. 2019;**72**(2):271–280. DOI: 10.1007/s42360-019-00133-w

[18] Habtu A Epidemiology of bean rust in Ethiopia. 1994;**172**. Available from: https://research.wur.nl/en/publications/epidemiology-of-bean-rust-in-ethiopia/ [Accessed: 2025-August-12]

[19] Wafula BW, Arunga EE, Rotich F. Prevalence and Host Resistance to Common Bean Rust Disease in Western and Central Kenya. International Journal of Agronomy. 2023;**2023**:19–54. DOI: 10.1155/2023/6064130

[20] Devi B. Variability Studies in Bean Rust (Uromyces Appendiculatus (Pers.) Unger) and Its Ecofriendly Management. Solan, Himachal Pradesh: University of Horticulture and Forestry (Nauni); 2019

[21] Souza T, Alzate-Marin A, Faleiro F, Barros E. Pathosystem common bean-Uromyces appendiculatus: Host resistance, pathogen specialization, and breeding for rust resistance. Pest Technology. 2008;**2**(2):56–69

[22] Pastor-Corrales MA. Sources, genes for resistance and pedigrees of 52 rust and mosaic resistant dry bean germplasm lines released by the USDA Beltsville bean project in collaboration with Michigan, Nebraska and North Dakota Agricultural Experiment Stations. Annual Report of the Bean Improvement Cooperative. 2003;**46**:235–241

[23] Koleva M, Kiryakov I. Resistance in common bean to uromyces appendiculatus under field and greenhouse conditions. Trakia Journal of Sciences. 2021;**19**(2):113–121. DOI: 10.15547/tjs.2021.02.001

[24] Todd AR, Donofrio N, Sripathi VR, McClean PE, Lee RK, Pastor-Corrales M, et al. Marker-assisted molecular profiling, deletion mutant analysis, and RNA-seq reveal a disease resistance cluster associated with uromyces appendiculatus infection in common bean phaseolus vulgaris L. International Journal of Molecular Sciences. 2017;**18**(6). DOI: 10.3390/ijms18061109

[25] de Souza TLPO, Dessaune SN, Sanglard DA, Moreira MA, de Barros EG. Characterization of the rust resistance gene present in the common bean cultivar Ouro Negro, the main rust resistance source used in Brazil. Plant Pathology. 2011;**60**(5):839–845. DOI: 10.1111/j.1365-3059.2011.02456.x

[26] Leitão ST, Rubiales D, Carlota M, Patto V. Identification of novel sources of partial and incomplete hypersensitive resistance to rust and associated genomic regions in common bean. BMC Plant Biology. 2023;1–15. DOI: 10.1186/s12870-023-04619-8

[27] Acevedo M, Steadman JR, Rosas JC. Uromyces appendiculatus in Honduras: Pathogen diversity and host resistance screening. Plant Disease. 2012;**97**(5):652–661. DOI: 10.1094/PDIS-02-12-0169-RE

[28] Hurtado-Gonzales OP, Diaz-Valderrama JR, Aime MC. Pastor-Corrales1 MA. Sequencing the complex genome of Uromyces appendiculatus, the bean rust pathogen. In Annual Report Bean Improvement Cooperative. 2018. p. 63–64

[29] Jochua C, Amane MIV, JR S, Xue X, Km E. Virulence Diversity of the Common Bean Rust Pathogen Within and Among Individual Bean Fields and Development of Sampling Strategies. Plant Disease. 2008;**92**(3):401–408. DOI: 10.1094/PDIS-92-3-0401

[30] Liebenberg MM, Pretorius ZA. Pathogenic Diversity in and Sources of Resistance to Uromyces appendiculatus in Southern Africa. Journal of Phytopathology. 2011;**159**(4):287–297. DOI: 10.1111/j.1439-0434.2010.01763.x

[31] Qi M, Mei Y, Grayczyk JP, Darben LM, Rieker MEG, Seitz JM, et al. Candidate Effectors From Uromyces appendiculatus, the Causal Agent of Rust on Common Bean, Can Be Discriminated Based on Suppression of Immune Responses. Frontiers in Plant Science. 2019;**10**(10):1–14. DOI: 10.3389/fpls.2019.01182/full

[32] Souza TLPO, Ragagnin VA, Dessaune SN, Sanglard DA, Carneiro JES, Moreira MA, et al. DNA marker-assisted selection to pyramid rust resistance genes in "carioca" seeded common bean lines. Euphytica. 2014;**199**(3):303–316. DOI: 10.1007/s10681-014-1126-0

[33] Osuna-Caballero S, Rispail N, Barilli E, Rubiales D. Management and breeding for rust resistance in legumes. Journal of Plant Pathology. 2024;**108**(2026). DOI: 10.1007/s42161–024–01679–z

[34] Makhumbila P, Rauwane M, Muedi H, Figlan S. Insights of Phaseolus vulgaris' response to infection by Uromyces appendiculatus using an RNA-seq approach. Frontiers in Plant Science. 2025;**16**. DOI: 10.3389/fpls.2025.1557954/full

[35] Ayyappan V, Kalavacharla V, Thimmapuram J, Bhide KP, Sripathi VR, Smolinski TG, et al. Genome-wide profiling of histone modifications (H3K9me2 and H4K12ac) and gene

expression in rust (Uromyces appendiculatus) inoculated common bean (Phaseolus vulgaris L). PLoS One. 2015;**10**(7):1–29. DOI: 10.1371/journal.pone.0132176

[36] Kaur B, Bhatia D, Mavi GS. Eighty years of gene-for-gene relationship and its applications in identification and utilization of R genes. Journal of Genetics. 2021;**100**(2):50. DOI: 10.1007/s12041-021-01300-7

[37] Omara RI, Kamel SM, El-Ganainy SM, Arafa RA, Mostafa YS, Alamri SA, et al. Host Resistance to Uromyces appendiculatus in Common Bean Genotypes. Plants. 2022;**11**(5):1–19. DOI: 10.3390/plants11050628

[38] Do VFXR, Parlevliet JE, Zambolim L. Concepts in plant disease resistance. Fitopatol Bras. 2001;**26**(3):577–589

[39] Assefa T, Assibi Mahama A, V. BA, Cannon EKS, Rubyogo JC, Rao IM, et al. A review of breeding objectives, genomic resources, and marker-assisted methods in common bean (Phaseolus vulgaris L.). Molecular Breeding. 2019;**39**(2). DOI: 10.1007/s11032-018-0920-0

[40] Koleva M, Kiryakov I. Resistance in Common Bean (Phaseolus Vulgaris L.) To Uromyces appendiculatus in Bulgaria. "Annals Univ Craiova - Agric Mont Cadastre Ser ". 2023;**52**(1):224–232. DOI: 10.52846/aamc.v52i1.1337

[41] Melmaiee K, Kalavacharla V, Brown A, Todd A, Thurston Y, Elavarthi S. Quantification and gene expression analysis of histone deacetylases in common bean during rust fungal inoculation. International Journal of Genomics. 2015;**2015**. DOI: 10.1155/2015/153243

[42] Nyang'au EK, Nyangeri JB, Makatiani J. Identification of bean rust (Uromyces appendiculatus) races on isolates collected from Nyamira county and Narok south sub county, Kenya. Annual Research and Review in Biology. 2016;**9**(3):1–7. DOI: 10.9734/ARRB/2016/23305

[43] Souza TLPO, Faleiro FG, Dessaune SN, de Paula TJ, Moreira MA, de Barros EG. Breeding for common bean (Phaseolus vulgaris L.) rust resistance in Brazil. Tropical Plant Pathology. 2013;**38**(5):361–374

[44] Mekonnen T, Haileselassie T, Identification TK. Mapping and Pyramiding of Genes/Quantitative Trait Loci (QTLs) for Durable Resistance of Crops to Biotic Stresses. Journal of Plant Pathology and Microbiology. 2017;**08**(06):1–14

[45] Mundt CC. Pyramiding for resistance durability: Theory and practice. Phytopathology. 2018;**108**(7):792–802. DOI: 10.1094/PHYTO-12-17-0426-RVW

[46] Kumari H, Corrales MAP, Rajapaksha RGAS, Bandaranayake PCG, Weebadde C. Characterization of Uromyces appendiculatus First Races in Sri Lanka and Identification of Genes for the Development of Rust-Resistant Snap Beans. Plant Disease. 2023;**107**(8):2431–2439. DOI: 10.1094/PDIS-08-22-1942-RE

[47] Kumar Joshi R, Nayak S. Gene pyramiding-A broad spectrum technique for developing durable stress resistance in crops. Biotechnology and

Molecular Biology Reviews. 2010;**5** (3):51–60

[48] Gupta S, Nadarajan N, Sen GD. Legumes in the omic era. Legume Omics Era. 2014;1–348. DOI: 10.1007/978-1-4 614-8370-0

[49] Diaz S, Ariza-Suarez D, Izquierdo P, Lobaton JD, de la Hoz JF, Acevedo F, et al Genetic mapping for agronomic traits in a MAGIC population of common bean (Phaseolus vulgaris L.). BMC Genomics. 2020;**21**:799

[50] Okii D, Tukamuhabwa P, Tusiime G, Talwana H, Odong T, Mukankusi C, et al. Agronomic qualities of genetic pyramids of common bean developed for multiple-disease-resistance. African Crop Science Journal 2017;**25**:457

[51] Alves SM, Lacanallo GF, Gonçalves-Vidigal MC, Vaz Bisneta M, Vidigal Rosenberg AG, Vidigal Filho PS. Genome-Wide Association for Morphological and Agronomic Traits in Phaseolus vulgaris L. Accessions. Plants. 2024;**13**(18):2638

[52] Odogwu BA, Nkalubo ST, Mukankusi C, Odong T, Awale HE, Rubaihayo P, et al. Phenotypic and genotypic screening for rust resistance in common bean germplasm in Uganda. Euphytica. 2017;**213**(2):1–14. DOI: 10.1 007/s10681-016-1795-y

[53] Kumari HM, Weebadde C, Rajapakshe RG, Corrales MA, Kusalani TL, Bandaranayake PC. Evaluation of Selected Local and Exotic Common Bean Germplasm for Genetic Resistance to Rust Pathogen Uromyces appendiculatus (Pers.). Tropical Agriculture. 2022;**170** (4):17–30

[54] Miklas PN, Stavely JR, Kelly JD. Identification and potential use of a molecular marker for rust resistance in common bean. Theoretical and Applied Genetics. 1993;**85**(6–7):745–749

[55] de Ma MDL, McClean PE, Steadman J, McCoy S, Markell S, Osorno JM. Bean rust resistance in the Guatemalan climbing bean germplasm collection. Legume Science. 2022;**4** (4):1–16. DOI: 10.1002/leg3.149

[56] Myles S, Boyko AR, Owens CL, Brown PJ, Grassi F, Aradhya MK, et al. Genetic structure and domestication history of the grape. Proceedings of the National Academy of Sciences of the United States of America. 2011;**108** (9):3530–3535. DOI: 10.1073/ pnas.1009363108

[57] Mukankusi C, Raatz B, Nkalubo S, Berhanu F, Binagwa P, Kilango M, et al. Genomics, genetics and breeding of common bean in Africa: A review of tropical legume project. Plant Breeding. 2019;**138**(4):401–414. DOI: 10.1111/ pbr.12573

[58] Aflitos SA, Sanchez-Perez G, de Ridder D, Fransz P, Schranz ME, de Jong H, et al. Introgression browser: High-throughput whole-genome SNP< visualization. The Plant Journal. 2015;**82**(1):174–182. DOI: 10.1111/tpj.12800

[59] Xu Y, Zhang X, Li H, Zheng H, Zhang J, Olsen MS, et al. Smart breeding driven by big data, artificial intelligence, and integrated genomic-enviromic prediction. Molecular Plant. 2022;**15** (11):1664–1695. DOI: 10.1016/ j.molp.2022.09.001

[60] Blasques GM, Dias LAS, Araújo MS, Chiorato AF,

Carbonell SAM, Corrêdo LP, et al. Enhancing enviromics based predictions in common bean multi-environment trials. Scientific Reports. 2025;**15**(1):1–16. DOI: 10.1038/s41598-025-21882-x

[61] Resende RT, Piepho HP, Rosa GJM, Silva-Junior OB, E Silva FF, de Resende MDV, et al. Enviromics in breeding: Applications and perspectives on envirotypic-assisted selection. Theoretical and Applied Genetics. 2021;**134**(1):95–112. DOI: 10.1007/s00122-020-03684-z

[62] Erfatpour M, Simons KJ, Roy J, Figueroa-Cerna JC, Lee R, Beaver J, et al. Fine mapping and identification of causal alleles at the Ur-11 locus controlling rust resistance in common bean (Phaseolus vulgaris L.). Theoretical and Applied Genetics. 2025;**138**(3):1–14. DOI: 10.1007/s00122-025-04836-9